YOUR MIRROR IMAGE

By Kathleen K. Collins
with Carol A. Kerr

Artwork by LaDonna Wright

Successful Images ™

5680 HERSHINGER CLOSE
DULUTH, GEORGIA 30097-6430
(770) 232-7101

LIBRARY OF CONGRESS CATALOGING IN PUBLICATION DATA

COLLINS, KATHLEEN K.
YOUR MIRROR IMAGE
ALL RIGHTS RESERVED.
ISBN 0-9621471-0-9

Copyright © 1987 By Kathleen K. Collins
Printed in the United States of America

First Printing 1987
Second Printing 1988
Third Printing 1989
Fourth Printing 1990
Fifth Printing 1993
Sixth Printing 1998

TABLE OF CONTENTS

CHAPTER I
THE WINNING ATTITUDE

Do you like yourself?

Have you ever been asked this question before? Actually, the question of liking yourself is one that encompasses many other questions. Do you like your appearance? your job? your financial position? your attitude? the way your future looks?

You are probably asking yourself, "What does attitude have to do with image and success?". The answer is, a lot! Eighty percent of success lies in attitude. The remaining 20 percent has to do with education, background, and past experience. It may be startling, but it's true! The Dale Carnegie Institute in New York did a research study on successful people and found that a positive attitude is the main key to their success. That's why attitude is the first subject of this book. You need to start working on your attitude immediately! It won't cost you one cent, and the results will be immeasurable.

Take a few moments now to **honestly** answer this question: Do you like yourself?

Many people cannot honestly say that they like everything about themselves. And, generally, the something that they don't like can be changed. Is there something you don't like about yourself? Then change it! You must like yourself **totally** before you can have total self-confidence.

Your attitude has a lot to do with liking yourself. Having the right attitude can, many times, take you farther than education or experience. When you believe in yourself and have confidence, other people will see this and respect it.

A study was once conducted where two groups, one all men and the other all women, were asked to write down everything that they didn't like about themselves. All of the men were through within three minutes, but the majority of the women still were not finished after fifteen minutes! Why?! Most women let fashion dictate to them too much. They try to be someone they don't want to be for others at the expense of themselves. We must all do what is right for ourselves, and having a winning attitude helps us do this.

This chapter is designed to help you improve your attitude. There is one important thing to remember when reading this chapter: We will be talking about many different points that have to do with attitude. If you are **honestly** satisfied with what you are or the way you do things with regard to any of the points talked about in this chapter, and it contradicts what is said here, forget what is said here. If you change yourself to do or be something you disagree with, how can you possibly like yourself? **Keep all of the points about yourself that you are satisfied with! You must first please yourself before you can please others!** All of us have, at some time or another, heard a "rags to riches" story, a success story of an average person who made it to the top on his own. One thing all of these successful people had in common was the right attitude. That winning attitude can work for you, too. Now, on to learning the ingredients of a winning attitude.

Cultivate a Winning Attitude

There are certain traits that go hand in hand with a winning attitude. Let's talk about these traits. The more of these traits you can incorporate into your attitude, the better your attitude will be.

Have **faith.** Believe that you are growing, that your entire life is improving. You should be able to look at yourself in the mirror every morning and say, "Today is going to be another great day!" If you are a sales person, have faith that you are going to close a big order. If you are a doctor, have faith that you will make your patients feel better.

Have **courage.** Let's face it – there are going to be minor setbacks along your road to success. But don't be afraid to try again. Frederick Wilcox said, "Progress always involves risk: you can't steal second base and keep your foot on first." Have the courage to try new things.

Be **generous.** People who are willing to share what they have with others, be it knowledge or a kind word, reap many benefits that will more than pay them back for their generosity. When you have an "I care about you" attitude, people remember and respect that.

Be the **individual** that you are. It is much easier to express yourself than imitate someone else. The whole idea of having a winning attitude is to be satisfied and happy with who **you** are. Look in the mirror and say, "I like who **I** am, and mean it!

Cooperate with others. There is probably not one successful person who made it to the top all by himself. You must be able to work well with others, listen, and share ideas.

Discourage a Losing Attitude

Along with items that your winning attitude should include, there are also items you should avoid to develop the best attitude possible. Let's look at these negative items, which you should do your best to eliminate from your personality.

Avoid **hate.** It is of no benefit to you to hate anyone. While no one can be expected to like everyone, being friendly to others will take you a lot farther than being unkind.

Don't **gossip.** This can be very detrimental to your career. Everyone makes mistakes, and it doesn't do anyone any good to talk about them. Having your name connected with gossip can only mean trouble.

Don't be **jealous** of the positions others are in. Be happy for others, and continue to strive toward your own goals. Have confidence that someday all you want will be yours, and someday it will be.

Don't **worry.** There are so many positive, constructive things you could be thinking about. Why clutter your mind with thoughts that will take you nowhere but backward? You should always strive for a feeling and look of total confidence.

Do not **fear** the unknown. If you give in to fear and fail to try, you will never know what you are capable of. Don't set limits for yourself before you even get started! One key to success is trying!

Let's look at some simple ideas that will help you in the quest for your winning attitude. The purpose of this list is to make your feel better about yourself, and also make others feel better about you.

1. Image is the perception that people have of you. But more importantly, it is the perception you have of yourself.

2. Remember that everything you will ever be comes **through** you, not **to** you. For example, if you feel successful, you will be successful. If you feel rich, you will attract riches.

3. Wear your personality on your back as well as on your face. Let all the world know who you are.

4. Every day you should wake up thinking postive thoughts. This sets the right mental mood for the day. Also, go to sleep thinking positive thoughts. This will guarantee a restful night.

5. Smile! Doing this can change your life!

6. No **one** should be more important to you than **you!**

7. Give yourself permission; permission to try, to succeed, to be happy, to have it all.

8. Don't let your clothing block your success. Look good, and you will feel a surge of confidence.

9. You cannot fail if just one person sees you as a success. That one person can be your boss, your spouse, your teacher, or your friend.

10. Remember that life is like a boomerang: Whatever you throw out will come back to you. If you give respect, you will receive respect. If you give love, you will receive love. If you cheat others, you will be cheated. If you lie to others, you will be lied to.

11. Walk with confidence. A confident walk is one where you kick from the hip, **not** from the knee.

12. Talk with confidence. A confident voice comes out loud and clear.

13. Remind yourself that golden opportunities await you each day. Be open to new opportunities. Really think about things before giving them a definite "no."

14. As you change, all conditions will change. As you improve, conditions will improve. As you succeed, conditions will help you continue to succeed.

15. All the world is a stage. It is your right to play the leading character on center stage. You are in control of your life. **You** will bring yourself riches or poverty.

16. It is your right to have everything you want in life, be it handsomeness or beauty, charm, prosperity, love, joy, peace. You have the ability to possess everything you want. But you must allow your abilities to come out from within.

17. Like yourself! This is really a powerful tool of success.

18. Poise is power.

19. Dress for your public. Your outward appearance should fit in with those you deal with.

20. The way you experience life is based on the way you choose to view what happens to you. Do you look at problems as negative things, or do you look at them as opportunities from which you can learn and grow?

21. Every morning you should look in the mirror and say to yourself, "I am the most fascinating person I know."

22. Self-love is self-acceptance. And self-acceptance leads to corporate acceptance.

23. If you look, think, and act like a winner, you will be a winner.

CHAPTER II
COLOR IMPACT

Color analysis was discovered over 45 years ago in Germany by an art professor named Johannes Itten. It was not well known until about ten years ago, and now millions of people around the world are following the theory of color analysis and receiving all of its benefits. Executives, politicians, doctors, lawyers, television personalites, men and women alike are all finding their naturally perfect colors that make them look younger, healthier, more slender, sophisticated, romantic, and authoritative.

Colors are divided into four palettes, which are described by the four seasons. By going through the steps below, you can determine which season you are, and then learn to make your colors work for you.

1. Take the following color quiz to find your season. Answer each question by circling the appropriate color group. The season in which you have the most circles will be your season.

    a. What is your skin tone?

Winter	Summer	Spring	Autumn
Light to dark gray beige Olive Black	Pale beige with pink cheeks Rose-beige Deep pink	Creamy ivory Peach-beige Golden beige	Ivory Creamy peach Light to dark golden beige

    B. What is your natural hair color?

Winter	Summer	Spring	Autumn
Medium to dark charcoal brown Blue-black White-blonde Silver-gray	Ash blonde Medium gray– Light to dark ash brown Blue-gray	Light to dark yellow blonde Taffy-red Gold-brown Pearl gray	Light to dark honey brown Red Chestnut Golden gray

    c. What is your eye color?

Winter	Summer	Spring	Autumn
Dark red-brown Hazel (brown with blue or green) Dark blue	Green Soft gray-blue Soft hazel (gray with blue or green)	Green Hazel blue/green Blue (clear)	Light to dark golden brown Deep olive Teal blue

    d. Which group of colors looks best on you?

Winter	Summer	Spring	Autumn
Charcoal gray Navy Royal blue Blue red Shocking pink	Blue gray Grayed navy Powder blue Burgundy Mauve	Medium gray Bright navy Peach/apricot Orange-red Bright aqua	Dark brown Grayed green Teal blue Rust Tomato red

e. Which shade of white do you wear best?

Winter	Summer	Spring	Autumn
Pure white	Soft white	Ivory	Oyster white

f. Which shade of blue do you wear best?

Winter	Summer	Spring	Autumn
Navy blue	Gray-blue	Light teal blue	Dark teal blue

g. Which shade of green do you wear best?

Winter	Summer	Spring	Autumn
Dark emerald	Blue-green	Bright yellow-green	Olive green

H. Which shade of pink do you wear best?

Winter	Summer	Spring	Autumn
Shocking pink	Powder pink	Coral pink	Salmon

2. Now that you have determined your season, you need to understand your palette, as some colors will be better for you than others. There may even be some colors in your palette that you should not wear near your face, although you could wear them below your waist, such as in slacks or shorts.

When trying on clothing in your right colors, always look to see what the color does for your face. We are too accustomed to trying on clothing and then looking into the mirror and admiring the garment, instead of asking ourselves, "What does this do for me?" Never allow your clothing (or makeup) to "wear" you. **You** wear your clothing!

Color swatches made out of fabric are available for you to purchase (see the order form in the back of this book), and they make shopping so much easier. When you go shopping, hold the swatches up to clothing to make sure that the garment is the right color for you. Chances are you won't find the exact shade of the swatch – shades on either side of the color are fine. Please don't limit yourself to the <u>exact</u> **shade** in the packet. You are only unnecesarily limiting yourself.

Be careful of store lighting, as it is artificial and can throw off color. This is why fabric swatches are so important; your swatch color will be thrown off, too, so the match will still be a valid match. If possible, take the garment and your swatches to a window. Otherwise, steer clear of direct artificial light. Comparing colors in a darker corner, away from direct artificial lighting, is the next best thing to a window. If you are color-blind, ask a salesperson for help.

Note: If you are interested in ordering fabric swatches of your season's colors, use the order form in the back of this book.

Following is a list of the different colors that are within each season's palette. First, the men's color palettes are given, followed by the women's color palettes. (Note that the colors in each palette are the same for both men and women; however, the articles of clothing for which the colors are used are different.)

MEN'S WINTER PALETTE

MEN'S WINTER PALETTE — Winters look best in clear colors and sharp contrast. Muted, powdered colors are not for the winter person. Winters should **think** true, blue, and vivid; sharp, clear, and icy.

WARDROBE:

Suits/Pants
(Neutral Colors)

Navy, charcoal gray, black, medium true gray, taupe (gray-beige), light true gray

Business/Dress Shirts
(Light Colors)

Pure white, icy pink, icy gray, icy green, icy blue, icy violet, icy yellow, icy aqua

Sport Coats
(Basic Colors)

True blue, blue-red, pine green, bright burgundy (also neutral colors above)

Sportswear
(Brights/accents)

Royal purple, true green, fuchsia, light true green, magenta, lemon yellow, deep hot pink, chinese blue, shocking pink, hot turquoise, true red, royal blue, emerald green

Ties

Colors from any group

Shoes and Belts

Black, navy, cordovan, gray, taupe (gray-beige), white

Overcoat

Black, navy, gray, taupe (gray-beige)

ACCESSORIES:

Jewelry

Silver, white gold, or platinum

MEN'S SUMMER PALETTE — Summer people wear soft neutrals especially well. They also look good in pastels. Soft colors rather than sharp contrasts are best for a summer person. Summers should **think** soft, rose, and blue; gentle.

WARDROBE:

Suits/Pants (Neutral Colors)	Grayed navy, rose-brown, charcoal blue-gray, cocoa, light blue-gray, rose-beige, grayed blue
Business/Dress Shirts (Light Colors)	Soft white, pale lemon yellow, light rose-beige, powder pink, powder blue, light mauve, light periwinkle blue, lavender
Sport Coats (Basic Colors)	Cadet blue, spruce green, burgundy, blue-red (also neutral colors above)
Sportswear (Brights/accents)	Light lemon yellow, pastel pink, sky blue, rose-pink, medium blue, deep rose, periwinkle blue, orchid, pastel aqua, mauve, pastel blue-green, raspberry, medium blue-green, soft fuchsia, deep blue-green, plum, watermelon red
Ties	Colors from any group
Shoes and Belts	Rose-brown, black, navy, cordovan, rose-beige, soft white
Overcoat	Navy, grayed blue, rose-brown, cocoa

ACCESSORIES:

Metal Jewelry	Silver, white gold, or platinum

MEN'S SPRING PALETTE

MEN'S SPRING PALETTE — Spring colors are all clear colors — nothing dark or muted. A spring person should **think** clear, yellow, lively, and crisp when shopping.

WARDROBE:

Suits/Pants
(Neutral Colors)

Clear bright navy, chocolate brown, medium warm gray, medium golden brown, light warm gray, golden tan, light warm beige, camel

Business/Dress Shirts
(Light Colors)

Ivory, warm pastel pink, buff, light clear blue, light peach/apricot, light periwinkle blue

Sport Coats
(Basic Colors)

Light clear navy, light teal blue, light clear gold, light rust (plus neutral colors above)

Sportswear
(Brights/accents)

Pastel yellow-green, bright golden yellow, bright yellow-green, peach/apricot, light warm aqua, clear salmon, clear bright aqua, clear bright warm pink, emerald turquoise, coral pink, light true blue, bright coral, periwinkle blue, light orange, dark periwinkle blue, orange-red, medium violet, clear bright red

Ties

Colors from any group

Shoes and Belts

Brown, tan, navy, cordovan (brownish), black (with navy), beige, ivory

Overcoat

Camel, medium warm gray, golden tan, light clear navy

ACCESSORIES:

Jewelry

Gold toned or brass

MEN'S AUTUMN PALETTE – Muted or clear colors are good for the autumn person. Deep colors are great for an autumn. **Think** gold and yellow undertones when shopping.

WARDROBE:

Suits/Pants (Neutral Colors)	Charcoal brown, camel, dark chocolate brown, marine navy, coffee brown, olive green, khaki/tan, grayed green
Business/Dress Shirts (Light Colors)	Oyster white, light peach/apricot, warm beige, light periwinkle blue, buff (light gold), light grayed green
Sport Coats (Basic Colors)	Forest green, gold, medium warm bronze, teal blue, rust, mahogany (plus neutral colors above)
Sportswear (Brights/accents)	Yellow-gold, bittersweet red, mustard, dark tomato red, pumpkin, jade green, terra-cotta, lime green, deep peach/apricot, moss green, salmon, bright yellow-green, orange, turquoise, orange-red, deep periwinkle blue
Ties	Colors from any group
Shoes and Belts	Brown, cordovan (brownish), black (with navy), tan, beige, oyster
Overcoat	Charcoal brown, coffee, camel, khaki/tan, marine navy

ACCESSORIES:

Jewelry	Gold, brass, or copper

WOMEN'S WINTER PALETTE – Winters look best in clear colors and sharp contrast. Muted, powdered colors are not for the winter person. Winters should **think** true, blue, and vivid; sharp, clear, and icy.

WARDROBE:

Suits/Pants/Skirts (Neutral Colors)	Navy, charcoal gray, black, medium true gray, taupe (gray-beige), light true gray
Business/Dress Blouses (Light Colors)	Pure white, icy pink, icy gray, icy green, icy blue, icy violet, icy yellow, icy aqua
Blazers (Basic Colors)	True blue, blue-red, pine green, bright burgundy (also neutral colors above)
Sportswear (Brights/accents)	Royal purple, true green, fuchsia, light true green, magenta, lemon yellow, deep hot pink, chinese blue, shocking pink, hot turquoise, true red, royal blue, emerald green
Scarves/Dresses	Colors from any group
Shoes and Belts	Black, navy, cordovan, gray, taupe (gray-beige), white
Overcoat	Black, navy, gray, taupe (gray-beige)

COSMETICS:

Foundation	Neutral beige or rose toned
Lips, Cheeks, Nails	Red, plum, pink, or burgundy
Eyeshadow	Gray or grayed tones

ACCESSORIES:

Hair	Your natural color is best, or ashtone if coloring
Jewelry Metals Stones Pearls	 Silver, white gold, or platinum Colors from your palette such as diamond, emerald, ruby or sapphire White or gray
Hosiery	Taupe, gray, navy, or black
Furs	A color from your season; white for evening

WOMEN'S SUMMER PALETTE — Summer people wear soft neutrals especially well. They also look good in pastels. Soft colors rather than sharp contrasts are best for a summer person. Summers should **think** soft, rose, and blue; gentle.

WARDROBE:

Suits/Pants/Skirts (Neutral Colors)	Grayed navy, rose-brown, charcoal blue-gray, cocoa, light blue-gray, rose-beige, grayed blue
Business/Dress Blouses (Light Colors)	Soft white, pale lemon yellow, light rose-beige, powder pink, powder blue, light mauve, light periwinkle blue, lavender
Blazers (Basic Colors)	Cadet blue, spruce green, burgundy, blue-red (also neutral colors above)
Sportswear (Brights/accents)	Light lemon yellow, pastel pink, sky blue, rose-pink, medium blue, deep rose, periwinkle blue, orchid, pastel aqua, mauve, pastel blue-green, raspberry, medium blue-green, soft fuchsia, deep blue-green, plum, watermelon red
Scarves/Dresses	Colors from any group
Shoes and Belts	Rose-brown, black, navy, cordovan, rose-beige, soft white
Overcoat	Navy, grayed blue, rose-brown, cocoa

COSMETICS:

Foundation	Neutral beige or rose toned
Lips, Cheeks, Nails	Pink, plum, rose, or burgundy
Eyeshadow	Soft grayed tones

ACCESSORIES:

Hair	Your natural color is best, or ashtone if coloring. Blondes may frost.
Jewelry **Metals** **Stones** **Pearls**	Silver, white gold or platinum, or rose gold Colors from your palette such as opal, ruby, sapphire, or aquamarine White or pink, also fresh water pearls
Hosiery	Rose or grayed beige, light gray or light navy
Furs	A color from your season; soft white for evening

WOMEN'S AUTUMN PALETTE — Muted or clear colors are good for the autumn person. Deep colors are great for an autumn. **Think** gold and yellow undertones when shopping.

WARDROBE:

Suits/Pants/Skirts
(Neutral Colors)

Charcoal brown, camel, dark chocolate brown, marine navy, coffee brown, olive green, khaki/tan, grayed green

Business/Dress Blouses
(Light Colors)

Oyster white, light peach/apricot, warm beige, light periwinkle blue, buff (light gold), light grayed green

Blazers
(Basic Colors)

Forest green, gold, medium warm bronze, teal blue, rust, mahogany (plus neutral colors above)

Sportswear
(Brights/accents)

Yellow-gold, bittersweet red, mustard, dark tomato red, pumpkin, jade green, terra-cotta, lime green, deep peach/apricot, moss green, salmon, bright yellow-green, orange, turquoise, orange-red, deep periwinkle blue

Scarves/Dresses

Colors from any group

Shoes and Belts

Brown, cordovan (brownish), black (with navy), tan, beige, oyster

Overcoat

Charcoal brown, coffee, camel, khaki/tan, marine navy

COSMETICS:

Foundation

Ivory, warm beige, or peach toned

Lips, Cheeks, Nails

Mocha, rust, dark peach, or cinnamon

Eyeshadow

Golden browns and greens

ACCESSORIES:

Hair

Your natural color is best or warm highlights if coloring

Jewelry
  Metals
  Stones
  Pearls

Gold, brass, or copper
Colors from your palette such as topaz, jade carnelian, or garnet
Creamy colored

Hosiery

Warm beige, suntan, brown or rust

Furs

A color from your season; creamy white for evening

WOMEN'S SPRING PALETTE – Spring colors are all clear colors – nothing dark or muted. A spring person should **think** clear, yellow, lively, and crisp when shopping.

WARDROBE:

Suits/Pants/Skirts
(Neutral Colors)
Clear bright navy, chocolate brown, medium warm gray, medium golden brown, light warm gray, golden tan, light warm beige, camel

Business/Dress Blouses
(Light Colors)
Ivory, warm pastel pink, buff, light clear blue, light peach/apricot, light periwinkle blue

Blazers
(Basic Colors)
Light clear navy, light teal blue, light clear gold, light rust (plus neutral colors above)

Sportswear
(Brights/accents)
Pastel yellow-green, bright golden yellow, bright yellow-green, peach/apricot, light warm aqua, clear salmon, clear bright aqua, clear bright warm pink, emerald turquoise, coral pink, light true blue, bright coral, periwinkle blue, light orange, dark periwinkle blue, orange-red, medium violet, clear bright red

Scarves/Dresses
Colors from any group

Shoes and Belts
Brown, tan, navy, cordovan (brownish), black (with navy), beige, ivory

Overcoat
Camel, medium warm gray, golden tan, light clear navy

COSMETICS:

Foundation
Ivory, warm beige, or peach toned

Lips, Cheeks, Nails
Peach, salmon, warm pink, or clear red

Eyeshadow
Light warm browns, greens, or blue greens

ACCESSORIES:

Hair
Your natural color is best or warm highlights if coloring

Jewelry
  Metals   Gold toned or brass
  Stones   Colors from your palette such as ivory, topaz, citrine, or coral
  Pearls   Creamy colored

Hosiery
Warm beige, ivory, or nude

Furs
A color from your season; creamy white for evening

CHAPTER III
BODY ARCHITECTURE

BODY SHAPES

Most of us do not have a perfect body shape, but we can create a perfect look. The whole "perfect" look is based on illusion, what the eye sees. Perhaps you are wider than average in the middle, or maybe your shoulders are too narrow. Some people are too tall, some too short. If you are too short, there is a line in clothing that will make you look taller. If you are too heavy, there is a line in clothing that will make you look thinner, and so on. Finding your right line in clothing will give your body the illusion of being perfect. By wearing the right clothes you can become taller, heavier, thinner, or whatever your particular need may be.

First you need to learn what is not perfect about your figure, and then you can use the charts in the book to determine the best clothing styles for you.

1. A well-proportioned figure is divided into four equal segments on both a man's and a woman's body:

- Head to underarm (first quarter)
- Underarm to hip (second quarter)
- Hip to knee (third quarter)
- Knee to feet (fourth quarter)

Take time to chart your body to find out if parts of your body are longer or shorter than they should be in relation to your overall height. Follow the steps listed here.

a. Tape a large piece of paper (at least 2 inches longer than you are tall) to a wall so that the bottom of the paper touches the floor. Any kind of paper can be used for this test — wide computer paper, newspaper, brown wrapping paper, etc.

b. Standing in front of the paper **with your shoes off,** have someone trace your outline onto the paper. If you use a black marker, you will most easily be able to see your outline on the paper. **Be extremely careful not to get any ink on your clothing.**

c. Now that the outline of your body has been drawn, mark the locations of your underarm, hip, and knee, (these divide the first, second, third, and fourth quarters of your body). To find the location of your hip, kick your leg straight out in front of you and mark where the top of the leg breaks. Bend your leg to find the location of your knee.

d. Also mark the location of your waist. (A perfectly proportioned waist will be exactly half way between your underarm and your hip.)

e. Remove the paper from the wall. Fold the paper back at the top of the head so that the top of your head is at the very top of the paper.

f. Lining up the top of the head and the bottom of the feet, fold the paper exactly in half, then fold it in half again. Unfold the sheet, and "you" are now divided into four equal segments, the four quarters we mentioned above. If the creases do not fall in the places indicated above, you are not perfectly proportioned. Don't worry — most people are not!!

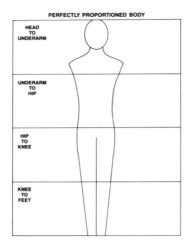

PERFECTLY PROPORTIONED BODY

HEAD TO UNDERARM

UNDERARM TO HIP

HIP TO KNEE

KNEE TO FEET

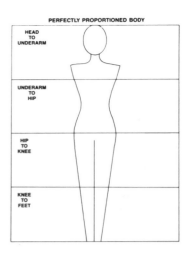

PERFECTLY PROPORTIONED BODY

HEAD TO UNDERARM

UNDERARM TO HIP

HIP TO KNEE

KNEE TO FEET

Here are sketches of perfect figures. Notice that the figures are divided by four solid lines, in the four places listed above.

LOW WAISTED AND SHORT LEGS

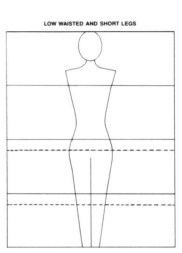

LOW WAISTED AND SHORT LEGS

Here are sketches of figures that have low waists and short legs. The solid lines mark the folds on the paper. The dotted lines mark the figures' underarms, hips, and knees. You should be able to see by comparing the two sets of lines that the figures have low waists and short legs.

Check here how you "measured up":

	Short	Average	Long
Head to underarm	_____	_____	_____
Underarm to hip	_____	_____	_____
Hip to knee	_____	_____	_____
Knee to feet	_____	_____	_____

If you are like most people, you are very surprised with what you have learned about your body proportion. It has been found that 95 percent of all people do not know their real body assets, and therefore they have dressed to show only their figure problems.

2. Take the time to fill out the following body and face shape chart. This will also be used to determine the best clothing styles for you. **Be honest with yourself!** If a certain part of your body is not proportioned, you must be willing to admit this point to better your overall appearance.

   Note that there are two different charts – one for men and one for women.

DO YOU FEEL YOU ARE:

a. Height   _____ Too Short   _____ Average   _____ Too Tall

b. Weight   _____ Proportioned   _____ Too Thin   _____ Too Heavy

c. Face Shape*   _____ Oval   _____ Diamond   _____ Pear

_____ Round   _____ Heart   _____ Oblong

_____ Square   _____ Triangle   _____ Rectangle

d. Neck length   _____ Proportioned   _____ Too Short   _____ Too Long

e. Neck width   _____ Proportioned   _____ Too Thin   _____ Too Thick

f. Shoulder shape **   _____ Proportioned   _____ Too Narrow   _____ Too Broad

g. Chest size   _____ Proportioned   _____ Too Small   _____ Too Large

h. Arm width (upper arm)   _____ Proportioned   _____ Too Thin   _____ Too Heavy

i. Arm length ***   _____ Proportioned   _____ Too Short   _____ Too Long

j. Waist Size   _____ Proportioned   _____ Too Small   _____ Too Large   (Rolls hanging over waist)

k. Waist length ****   _____ Proportioned   _____ Too High   _____ Too Low

l. Hip width **   _____ Proportioned   _____ Too Small   _____ Too Large

m. Leg width (thigh)   _____ Proportioned   _____ Too Thin   _____ Too Heavy

n. Leg length   _____ Proportioned   _____ Too Short   _____ Too Long

o. Protruding abdomen   Yes   No

p. Prominent derriere   Yes   No

q. Flat derriere   Yes   No

---

  * Information to help you determine your face shape is included later in this section, page 41.

  ** Proportioned shoulders are two inches broader than widest part of your hips. Narrow shoulders are less than two inches. Broad shoulders are more than two inches.

  *** Proportioned arms have the wrist even with the hip-socket area. Short arms are above the hip-socket. Long arms are below the hip-socket.

  **** If you are high waisted, you look best in a lower rise pant with a narrow belt 1/2" to 1" wide to slenderize the waist area. Also, blouson your shirts out over the belt. Do not tuck in tight! If you are low waisted, you look best in a higher rise pant with a wider belt 1" to 1-1/4" wide. Tuck shirt into pants as tight as possible. Do not blouson your shirt over your belt. It will add weight to you and enlongate your torso.

DO YOU FEEL YOU ARE:

a. Height	_____ Too Short	_____ Average	_____ Too Tall
b. Weight	_____ Proportioned	_____ Too Thin	_____ Too Heavy
c. Face Shape*	_____ Oval	_____ Diamond	_____ Pear
	_____ Round	_____ Heart	_____ Oblong
	_____ Square	_____ Triangle	_____ Rectangle
d. Neck length	_____ Proportioned	_____ Too Short	_____ Too Long
e. Neck width	_____ Proportioned	_____ Too Thin	_____ Too Thick
f. Shoulder shape **	_____ Proportioned	_____ Too Narrow	_____ Too Broad
g. Chest size	_____ Proportioned	_____ Too Small	_____ Too Large
h. Arm width (upper arm)	_____ Proportioned	_____ Too Thin	_____ Too Heavy
i. Arm length ***	_____ Proportioned	_____ Too Short	_____ Too Long
j. Waist Size	_____ Proportioned	_____ Too Small	_____ Too Large (Rolls hanging over waist)
k. Waist length ****	_____ Proportioned	_____ Too High	_____ Too Low
l. Hip width	_____ Proportioned	_____ Too Small	_____ Too Large
m. Leg width (thigh)	_____ Proportioned	_____ Too Thin	_____ Too Heavy
n. Leg length	_____ Proportioned	_____ Too Short	_____ Too Long
o. Protruding abdomen	Yes No		
p. Prominent derriere	Yes No		
q. Flat derriere	Yes No		

* Information to help you determine your face shape is included later in this section, page 41.

** Proportioned shoulders are two inches broader than widest part of your hips. Narrow shoulders are less than two inches. Broad shoulders are more than two inches.

*** Proportioned arms have the wrist even with the hip-socket area. Short arms are above the hip-socket. Long arms are below the hip-socket.

**** High waisted women look best in narrow belts 1/2" to 1" wide or 3" wide curved style belts that rest on the hip. Chain belts are also a great look on her. Always match your belt to your blouse or totally contrast the color from the blouse and skirt color. Also, blouson your tops. Low waisted women look best in wider belts 2" or more. Match belt color to skirt or totally contrast the color from the blouse and skirt color. Also, tuck tops in as tight as possible. DO NOT BLOUSON.

3. Now that you know your body architecture, it is time to learn to use lines to make you look in perfect proportion. The simple fact is: The eye naturally travels along lines. Therefore, have lines running across your good points.

The proper belt can enhance your perfectly proportioned waist, or it can correct a waist that is out of proportion. If your waist is perfectly proportioned halfway between your underarm and your hip, the belt for you is one whose width is one inch. If your waist is one-half inch too low, you should wear a 1-½" belt. If your waist is one inch too low, wear a 2" belt. If your waist is one-half inch high, a ½" belt is best for you. And if your waist is one inch high, very thin belts, such as cord belts, are best. Men shouldn't wear belts any narrower than ½ inch or any wider than 1-½ inches. Men that are 2" or more low waisted can wear slacks with wider waist bands. (Most of these type of slacks do not require a belt to be worn with the slack.) This type of slack will prevent a man's shirt from coming out of his slacks when he sits or bends. It also will be his most comfortable pair of slacks if he is low waisted.

With regard to shorts for both men and women, you first need to find the widest part of your hips. To do this, stand with your feet flat on the floor. Feel along your upper legs with your fingertips, and locate the widest part of your legs. If your legs are thin, this point is the ideal length for shorts, because it will make your legs appear heavier. If your legs are average or heavy, wear your shorts two inches or more above the widest part of your legs, or two inches or more below the widest part of your legs. Angled or athletic cut shorts will make your legs appear longer and, in some cases, thinner. Note For Women: This rule also applies to a women's perfect jacket length. This is not true for a man's jacket length. A man's perfect jacket length can be determined by the following measurement. Wearing a jacket and shoes, measure from the bottom of the jacket collar to the floor. Divide this number in half and this is your perfect jacket length. This rule is accurate 100% of the time!

4. Fill in the following clothing charts using the information you gathered in step 2. Running down the left side of each chart are figure "problems." Place a check mark in the box next to those items that apply to you. Reading across the chart you will see X's and some O's. An "X" means that the style is the best style for you to camouflage that particular figure flaw. An "O" means avoid this style as it will make your problem look worse than it really is. A blank means the style is okay, not terrific but O.K. **Two filled-in sample charts, along with explanations of how to "read" them, follow the clothing charts that you fill in.**

Sample Charts and How to Read Them

This chart shows mens' jacket styles. The man for whom this chart was filled out has three figure flaws: he is short, heavy and has a prominent derriere, and these items are marked on the left side of the chart. Let's look at jacket styles for short men first. The first style is marked with an "O," which means that this style should be avoided by short men. Therefore, we have crossed out this style. The other "O" styles farther down the line are crossed out, also. The next two styles are marked with "X"s, which means that these styles are excellent for a short man. There is one jacket style that has a blank, which means it is not the best, but it is O.K. for a short man.

Now let's look at the jacket styles that are excellent for men that are heavy. These jacket styles have "X"s, which means that these styles are excellent for a heavy man. The three styles with "O"s should be avoided. There are four styles with blanks, which mean they are not the best, but are O.K. for a heavy man.

Next let's look at the jacket styles that are excellent for men with prominent derrieres. Only one jacket has an "X," which means that this is the best jacket style for a prominent derriere.

Now let's look at the three figure flaws together. Count the number of "X"s next to each figure flaw. The two button, three button and one vent jackets all receive two "X"s which means that they correct two of this man's three figure problems. The Updated American (Tapered) Jacket received one "X", therefore correcting one of his three figure flaws. The Close Double Breasted Jacket just received an O.K. Why wear an O.K. style when you can wear an excellent one!

MENS JACKET STYLES:

	Single Button ✗	Two Button (2)	Three Button (2)	Close Double Breasted (OK)	Spread Double Breasted ✗	One Vent (2)	Two Vented ✗	No Vent ✗	Ivy League (Boxy) ✗	Updated American (Tapered) (1)			
Height: Short	O	X	X		O	X	X	X	O	X			
Height: Tall	X	X	O		X	X	X	X	X				
Weight: Thin	X	X	O	X	X		X		O	X			
Weight: Heavy	O	X	X		O		O		X				
Waist Small	X		O	X	X			X	X				
Waist Large	O	X	X		O				X				
Flat Derriere							X						
Prominent Derriere						X	O	O					

X = EXCELLENT FOR YOUR BODY TYPE
O = AVOID
Blank Space = Good

26

This chart shows womens' dress styles. The woman for whom this chart was filled out has five figure flaws: she is short, heavy, has narrow shoulders, has a large bust, and is low waisted. Because this chart is read the same way as the one explained previously, you know that we can cross out all dress styles with "O"s under them. This eliminates the empire because of the large bust, the wrap because of the narrow shoulders and large bust, the tunic because of the large bust, the dropped waist because of the short height, heavy weight and large bust, and the tent because of the short height.

Now, when you go through and count the number of "X"s next to each figure flaw, you will find that the sheath has five "X"s, which means that it **corrects** all five figure problems. This style is best for this woman. It will make her look like she has a perfect shape.

You should **not** wear a style, even if it has a lot of "X"s, if it has any "O"s, because the "O"s will accent your flaws.

DRESS STYLES:	Shift (4)	A-Line (3)	Fitted Shift (3)	Princess (3)	Shirt Waist (4)	Sheath (5)	~~Empire~~	~~Wrap~~	~~Tunic~~	Yoke (5)	~~Dropped Waist~~	~~Tent~~
☑ Height: Short	X			X	X	X	X	X	O	X	O	O
☐ Height: Tall		X		O		X	O	X	X	O	X	X
☐ Weight: Thin	X	X	X	O		X	X	X	X	X	X	X
☑ Weight: Heavy	X	X	X	X	X	X		X	O	X	O	X
☑ Narrow Shoulders						X		O		X		
☐ Broad Shoulders				X	X			X		O		
☐ Small Bust				X	X	X	X			X		
☑ Large Bust	X	X	X		X	X	O	O	X	X	X	X
☐ High Waisted	X	X	X	X	X		X		X	X	X	X
☑ Low Waisted	X	X	X	X	X	X	X		X	X	X	X
☐ Small Hips	X	X	X		X	X	X	X	X	X	X	X
☐ Large Hips	O	X		X	X	O	O	O	O	O	X	X
☐ Short Legs	X	O		X		X			O	X	O	O
☐ Long Legs	O	X		O		O			X	O	X	X

X = EXCELLENT FOR YOUR BODY TYPE
O = AVOID
Blank Space = Good

Successful Images®

Once you have filled out the charts by marking which figure flaws apply to you, you may have a situation where two or more figure flaws will be corrected by the same style of clothing. That's great! It is also possible, however, that you will need different styles of clothing to correct different figure flaws. If this is the case, you must try to strike a happy medium. It is possible that two of the styles shown will be combined in one garment. Or, you can avoid the style altogether. **This is a trial and error task.** You simply have to learn at this point which style will make you look your best. The easiest way to do this is have an honest friend tell you how a garment looks on you. Also use the opinion of a salesperson or other person who does not know you. It is very difficult to be objective with yourself.

If you have an "X" and an "O" under the same style, it is best to avoid that style. Even though one figure flaw will be hidden, another flaw will be greatly accented. Don't look "semi" good; look terrific, all over, all the time.

MENS JACKET STYLES:

	Single Button	Two Button	Three Button	Double Breasted	Double Breasted	One Vent	Two Vented	No Vent	Ivy League (Boxy)	Updated American (Tapered)
☐ Height: Short	O	X	X		O	X	X	X	O	X
☐ Height: Tall	X	X	O		X	X	X	X	X	
☐ Weight: Thin	X	X	O	X	X		X		O	X
☐ Weight: Heavy	O	X	X	X	O		O		X	X
☐ Waist: Small	X		O	X	X				X	X
☐ Waist: Large	O	X	X		O				X	
☐ Flat Derriere							X			
☐ Prominent Derriere						X	O	O		

X = EXCELLENT FOR YOUR BODY TYPE

O = AVOID

Blank Space = Good

Jacket Length:
_____ inches (see below for measuring instructions)

NOTE: JACKET LENGTH. With shoes on, jacket on and buttoned, legs together, measure from back collar jacket seam to floor. Divide that amount in half. Your jacket should be within one inch above or below that amount. I recommend going to the one longer rather than the shorter if you have a choice. Suit looks richer longer.

Successful Images®

	High-cut Bikini	Boxer Shorts (high cut)	Boxer Shorts	Surfer "Jams"	Boxer Shorts (w/ cuffs)	Elastic Waistband	Fitted Waistband	Walking Shorts	Short Waistband	High Waistband	Forward Pleats *	Reverse Pleats *	Cuffed
Height: Short	X	X	O	O	O			O					O
Height: Tall	O	O	X	X	X			X					X
Weight: Thin	X	O	X	X	X	X		X				X	
Weight: Heavy	O	X		O	O	O	X	X			X		
Small Hips	X		X	X	X	X					O	X	
Large Hips	O	X		O	O	O	X	X			X	O	
Thin Legs	O			X	X			X				X	X
Heavy Legs	O	X	O	O	O			O					O
Short Legs	X	X		O	O			O					O
Long Legs	O	O	X	X	X		X	X				X	X
High Waisted	X	O		X	X				X	O			X
Low Waisted	O	X	O	O	O				O	X			O
Protruding Abdomen	O		O	O		O	X				X	X	O

X = EXCELLENT FOR YOUR BODY TYPE

O = AVOID

Blank Space = Good

* If you have a protruding stomach, tack pleats down two inches from waistband to hold pleats down and stomach in.

COLLAR AND NECKLINE STYLES:

	Ascot	High Standing Collar	Low Standing Collar	Turtleneck	Mock Turtleneck	Mandarin	Crew Neck	V-Neck	Boat Neck	Raglan Sleeve
☐ Weight: Thin	O			X						
☐ Weight: Heavy	X			O	X					
☐ Neck: Short		O	X	O	X			X		
☐ Neck: Long		X	O	X	O	X		O		
☐ Neck: Thin	X	X		X		X		O	X	
☐ Neck: Thick				O	X	X		X	O	
☐ Narrow Shoulders									X	O
☐ Broad Shoulders									O	X

X = EXCELLENT FOR YOUR BODY TYPE

O = AVOID

Blank Space = Good

WOMEN'S DRESS STYLES:

Body Type	Shift	A-Line	Fitted Shift	Princess	Shirt Waist	Sheath	Empire	Wrap	Tunic	Yoke	Dropped Waist	Tent
☐ Height: Short	X			X	X	X	X	X	O	X	O	O
☐ Height: Tall		X		O		X	O	X	X	O	X	X
☐ Weight: Thin	X	X	X	O		X	X	X	X	O	X	X
☐ Weight: Heavy	X	X	X	X	X	X		X	O	X	O	X
☐ Narrow Shoulders						X		O*		X		
☐ Broad Shoulders				X	X			X		O		
☐ Small Bust	X				X		X	X		X		
☐ Large Bust	X	X	X	O	X	X	O	O	X	X	X	X
☐ High Waisted	X	X	X	X	X		X		X	X	X	X
☐ Low Waisted	X	X	X	X	X	X	X		X	X	X	X
☐ Small Hips	X	X	X		X	X	X	X	X	X	X	X
☐ Large Hips	O	X		X	X	O	O	O	O	X	O	X
☐ Short Legs	X	O		X			X		O	X	O	O
☐ Long Legs	O	X		O			O		X	O	X	X

X = EXCELLENT FOR YOUR BODY TYPE

O = AVOID

Blank Space = Good

* = Ok if you add shoulder pads.

DRESS AND SKIRT LENGTH: To make legs appear thinner go above or below calf-muscle area. To make the leg appear heavier, go across the widest part of the calf-muscle. Shorter lengths make you appear taller!

WOMEN'S JACKET STYLES:

Body Type	Vest	Bolero	Fitted	Semi-Fitted	Unfitted	Single-Breasted	Chanel	Close Double Breasted	Spread Double Breasted	One Vent	Two Vented	No Vent
☐ Height: Short	X	X	X	X	X	X	O**		O	X	X	X
☐ Height: Tall		O	O	X	X	X	X		X	X	X	X
☐ Weight: Thin	X	O	O	X	X	X	X	X	X		X	
☐ Weight: Heavy	O	X	O	X	X	X	X		O		O	
☐ Narrow Shoulders	O*											
☐ Broad Shoulders	X											
☐ Small Bust	X		X									
☐ Large Bust	O		O									
☐ High Waisted	X	O										
☐ Low Waisted	O	X			X							
☐ Small Hips	X		X						X			
☐ Large Hips	O	O	O	X		X			O			
☐ Short Legs	X	X					O					
☐ Long Legs	O	O					X					

X = EXCELLENT FOR YOUR BODY TYPE

O = AVOID

Blank Space = Good

* Ok if you wear shoulder pads.

** Ok with shorter skirt (knee-cap area).

JACKET LENGTH: To slenderize thighs go below widest part of thigh 2″ or more. Longer jackets look more business like. Shorter jackets look more social.

Successful Images®

33

WOMEN'S
NECKLINE STYLES:

	Jewel	Scoop	V-Neck	U-Neck	Square	Bateau	Halter
☐ Weight: Thin							O
☐ Weight: Heavy							O
☐ Neck: Short	X	X	X	X	X	X	
☐ Neck: Long	X	O*	O*	O*	O*	X	
☐ Neck: Thin	X	X	O	X	X	X	O
☐ Neck Thick	X	O	X	O	O	O	X
☐ Narrow Shoulders	X	X	X	X	X	X	O
☐ Broad Shoulders	X	O	X	X	O	O	X
☐ Small Bust							X
☐ Large Bust							O

X = EXCELLENT FOR YOUR BODY TYPE

O = AVOID

Blank Space = Good

* Ok with choker style necklace or scarf.

COLLAR STYLES:

Body Type	Tie	Ascot	High Standing	Wing	Turtleneck **	Cowl	Ruffle	Peter Pan	Puritan	Mandarin	Closed Convertible	Convertible	Sailor
Weight: Thin	X	X			X	X	X	X					
Weight: Heavy	O	O			O	O	O	O					X
Neck: Short	O	O	O	X	O	O	O	O	O			X	X
Neck: Long	X	X	X	X	X	X	X	X	X	X	X	O	O
Neck: Thin	X	X	X	X	X	X	X	O	X	X		X	X
Neck: Thick	O	O		O	O	O	O	X	O	X	X	X	
Narrow Shoulders				X	X	X		O*	X			X	X
Broad Shoulders	X	X	X	O	X	O	X	X	O	X	X	X	O
Small Bust	X	X			X		X		X				
Large Bust	O	O			O	O	O		O			X	O

X = EXCELLENT FOR YOUR BODY TYPE

O = AVOID

Blank Space = Good

* Ok with shoulder pads.
** Mock Turtleneck is ok for shorter necks.

WOMEN'S SLEEVE STYLES:

Body Type	Sleeveless	Capped	Short	Three-Quarter	Long	Long, Cuffed	Full	Raglan	Leg O' Mutton	Bell	Gathered	Dolman
Height: Short	X			X			O		X			O
Height: Tall	O			O			X		O			X
Narrow Shoulders	O	X						O*	X		X	O*
Broad Shoulders	X							X	O		O	X
Small Bust			X						X		X	
Large Bust			O						O		O	O
Thin Arms	O	O	O	X	X	X	X					X
Heavy Arms	O	O	O	X	X	X	X	X	O	X		X
Short Arms	X	X	X		X				X			X
Long Arms	O	X	X			X	X		O			X
Small Hips							O					
Large Hips												

X = EXCELLENT FOR YOUR BODY TYPE

O = AVOID

Blank Space = Good

* Ok with shoulder pads.

36

WOMEN'S SKIRT STYLES:

Body Type	Straight	A-Line	Flared	Dirndl	Center Seam	Gathered	Pleated	Stitched Pleats	Narrow Center Panel	Wide Center Panel	Wrap
☐ Height: Short	X	O		X	X				X	O	
☐ Height: Tall	O	X	X	X	O	X	X	X	O	X	
☐ Weight: Thin			X	X	O	X	X	X	O	X	
☐ Weight: Heavy	O			X	X		O	O	X	O	
☐ High Waisted						O					
☐ Low Waisted						X					
☐ Small Hips	X	X	X	X	X	X	X	X	X	X	X
☐ Large Hips	O	X	X	X	X	X	O	O	X	X	X
☐ Thin Legs	X	X	X	X	X	X	X	X	X	X	X
☐ Heavy Legs	O	X	X	X	X	X	X	X	X	X	X
☐ Short Legs	X	O									
☐ Long Legs	O	X									
☐ Protruding Abdomen	O	O	X	X		X	O	O	X		

X = EXCELLENT FOR YOUR BODY TYPE

O = AVOID

Blank Space = Good

WOMEN'S SLACK STYLES:

	No Waist Band	High Waist Band	Gathered	On-Seam Pockets	Slant Pockets	Fly Front	Plain Front	Tapered	Straight	Forward Pleats*	Reverse Pleats*	Cuffed	Flared
Height: Short	X							X	X			O	O
Height: Tall	O							O	X			X	X
High Waisted		O										X	
Low Waisted		X										O	
Small Hips			X	X	O			X	X	O	X		
Large Hips			O	O	X	X	X	O	X	X	O		
Thin Legs								O	X	X	X	X	X
Heavy Legs								O	X	X	X	O	X
Short Legs	X	X										O	O
Long Legs		O					O					X	X
Protruding Abdomen			O	O	X					X	X		

X = EXCELLENT FOR YOUR BODY TYPE

O = AVOID

Blank Space = Good

* If you have a protruding stomach, tack pleats down two inches from waistband to hold pleats

WOMEN'S SHORTS STYLES:

	Short Shorts	Walking Shorts	Below Knee Shorts	Culottes
☐ Height: Short	X	X	O	O
☐ Height: Tall	O	X	X	X
☐ High Waisted	O	X	X	X
☐ Low Waisted	X	X	X	X
☐ Small Hips	X	X	X	X
☐ Large Hips	O	X	X	X
☐ Thin Legs	X	X	X	X
☐ Heavy Legs	O	X	X	X
☐ Short Legs	X	X	O	O
☐ Long Legs	O	X	X	X

X = EXCELLENT FOR YOUR BODY TYPE

O = AVOID

Blank Space = Good

SHORTS LENGTH: To make legs appear thinner, shorts should be 2" or more below widest part of thigh. To make legs appear heavier, shorts should be right at widest part of thigh or go longer and add cuffs. This adds bulk to the leg.

WOMEN'S SWIMSUIT STYLES:

	Strapless Solid One Piece	Strapless Patterned One Piece	Solid One Piece	Detailed One-Piece	Adjustable	Foldable	Ruffles	Skirted	Shorted	High-Cut Bikini
☐ Weight: Thin	O	X	X	X	O	O	O			O
☐ Weight: Heavy	X	O	X	X	O	O	O	X	X	O
☐ Small Bust		X		X	O	X	X	X		X
☐ Large Bust	O	O	X		X	O	O		O	O
☐ High Waisted	X	X	X		X	X	X	X	X	
☐ Low Waisted	X	X	X		O	O	O	O	X	
☐ Small Hips		X	X		O	O	X	X	X	O
☐ Large Hips	X	O	X	X	O	O	O	X	X	O
☐ Thin Legs		X	X					X	X	O
☐ Heavy Legs			X		O	O	O	X	X	O
☐ Short Legs	X	X	X		O	O	O	O	O	X
☐ Protruding Abdomen	O		X	X	O	O	O	O		O

X = EXCELLENT FOR YOUR BODY TYPE

O = AVOID

Blank Space = Good

FACE SHAPES

The perfect face shape is oval. The goal of all other face shapes is to look oval by wearing the appropriate hair and eyeglass style. Mens' collars and womens' earring styles can also help give the illusion of a perfectly shaped face.

You can determine the shape of your face in one of two ways:

1. Pull your hair away from your face. You must be able to see your hairline. Then have a friend look straight at you to tell you what your face shape is.

   or

2. Pull your hair away from your face. Then look into a mirror and outline your face on the mirror with a lipstick or a bar of soap. Stand back and look at the shape you have drawn.

   It is possible that your face shape may be a combination of two shapes. For example, your face may be oval at the jawline, but square at the temples. Because the perfect face shape is oval, you should concentrate on tips for the square face. If your face is a combination of round and square, you should combine the information given for the two shapes.

Here are some overall hints for both men and women, and then we will go on to all of the possible face shapes. Again, all face shapes will be discussed as they apply to men, followed by face shapes as they apply to women

Hair Style Hints:

The secret to creating the best hairstyle for a face is: Where you have it, take away; where you don't have it, add.

For example, if you have a wide face, you don't want much hair on the sides of the face because it will make your face look even wider. **Take away** from this area by wearing your hair closer or shorter at the sides. However, you want your face to look longer than it is. **Add to it** by wearing your hair high on the top of your head and wearing some length at the collar.

Another example: If your face is heart-shaped or triangular, you have wide temples and a narrow chin. **Take away** from your temples, by wearing hair close to the head in this area. **Add to** the chin area by wearing more length and fullness.

If your eyes slant down on the outer edge, it is important to brush your hair up and back. If your eyes slant up, you can brush your hair up or down. The proper direction of your hair with regard to your eyes will make you appear more awake and alert.

"GRAVITY PULLS YOU DOWN, SO EVERYTHING THAT YOU WEAR AND DO TO YOUR BODY SHOULD AUTOMATICALLY PULL YOU UP!!!"

Eyeglass Hints:

The basic rules to selecting the eyeglasses and sunglasses that are perfect for you are:

1. Choose a color that is appropriate for your hair, skin, and eye color (refer to Chapter 2). This can also be the metal of your season (gold or silver).

2. The top of the eyeglass's frame should be perfectly even with your eyebrows. (You do not want to look like you have four eyebrows.)

3. When trying eyeglasses, smile your biggest, brightest smile! The bottom of the eyeglass's frame should not cut off your smiling cheeks, nor should it cut into your cheeks.

4. Look at yourself in the mirror while wearing the eyeglasses. If you have a wide face, the sides of the frames should be within the sides of your face. If you have a narrow face, the sides of the frames should extend beyond the sides of your face.

5. The bridge of the frames should be high if you have a short nose. If your nose is long, you will look better in frames with a low bridge.

6. The stems should go straight across at your temples from the top of the frames. Stay away from low or curved stems, they make the face appear longer and tired! Gravity pulls you down, so everything you wear should automatically pull you up!

7. Frameless bottom frames take away darkness under the eye. They tend to make the eye area look younger and brighter.

8. Avoid tinted lenses for daily wear. Why do you want to hide the natural beauty of your eyes?! Tinted lenses make you look old and tired, and it also makes you look as though you are trying to hide behind your glasses. If you have sensitive eyes, and therefore must use a tint, use the lightest shade possible! Remember that the eye is the most beautiful part of the human body, and everything you wear should complement your eyes!

All of the possible face shapes follow, with the best hair and eyeglass styles for each shape. Place and "X" next to the shape of your face. Then, when you have your hair styled or buy new eyeglasses, use the corresponding tips so that you will achieve your best look.

Necktie Hints For Men:
If you have a wide face, you should tie your tie with a half windsor knot. This style knot is wider, so it will balance with your wider face, making it look in perfect proportion. If you have a thin face, tie your tie with a four-in-hand knot. Because it is a narrower knot, it will balance with your thin face, making it look in perfect proportion.

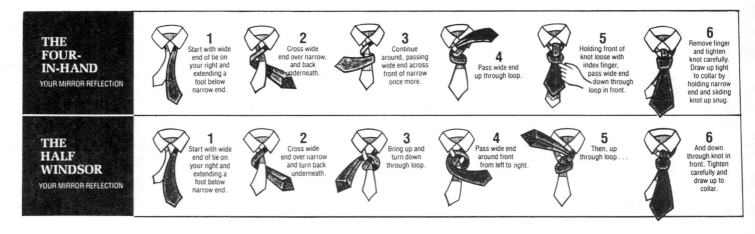

MEN'S OVAL FACE

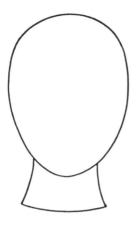

This is the ideal face shape. The width of an oval face is roughly 2/3 of the face length. The forehead is usually slightly wider than the chin, and there is no squareness in the chin.

If your face is oval, your goal is to maintain the natural balance (perfect proportion) of your facial features.

Hair: You can wear almost any hair style, although simple styles are best. Just be sure that you keep your hair in proportion with the rest of you.

Glasses: You can wear any frame that is not extreme (too small, too large, or too angular).

Collars: Any style that suits your personality is good. You should avoid extremes, however, as they can throw off the natural balance of your face.

MEN'S ROUND FACE

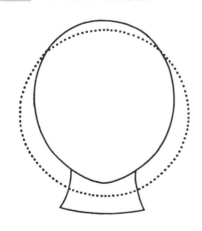

A round face is almost as wide as it is long. It is wide across the cheekbones – a very full face.

If your face is round, your goal is to slim your face and create a longer look, by narrowing your cheekbones and adding width at your forehead and jaw.

Hair: Strive to add fullness on top of the head, at the same time keeping hair short around the ears. A side part will break up the roundness, as will hair angled on the forehead. Sideburns should be slightly long and angled. A beard can make your jawline appear more angular.

Glasses: Frames that are straight across the top are best. Sides that angle in will create a slimmer look. Avoid very square and round styles.

Collars: Collars that have an average to slightly long length will make your face appear longer. An average to slightly narrow spread will also give your face the needed length.

MEN'S RECTANGLE or OBLONG FACE

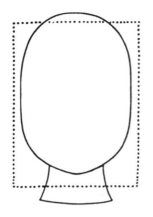

An oblong face is long and angular. The forehead, cheekbones, and jaw all have roughly the same width.

If your face is oblong, your goal is to add width to your face and minimize its length.

Hair: Add fullness at the temples and sides of the face. Having a side part with hair angled on the forehead shortens the face. Keep hair short in back. A straight mustache can make your face appear wider.

Glasses: Your best frames are those that are slightly heavy (shortens the face), slightly square (diminishes facial angles), and slightly wide (widens the face).

Collars: A collar of average to slightly short length is good. For the best possible look, the collar should have a slightly wide spread.

MEN'S PEAR

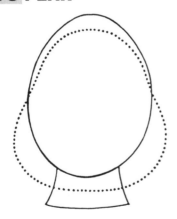

This shape face is characterized by a narrow forehead and wide jawline.

If your face is pear-shaped, your goal is to add fullness at the crown and temples, and to narrow your jaw.

Hair: Add fullness at the temples and sides of the face. A side part is good. Keeping some hair on the neck that is visible from the front will soften the jawline.

Glasses: Choose frames that are wide at the temple, because they will make the upper half of your face appear wider. Choosing a frame that is somewhat heavy across the top is also good for this purpose.

Collars: Collars that have an average to slightly long length will make your face appear longer. An average to slightly narrow spread will also give your face the needed length.

MEN'S SQUARE FACE

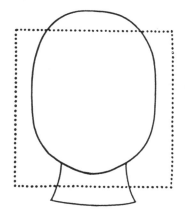

A square face is characterized by a forehead, cheekbones, and jaw that are all about the same width. The face isn't much longer than it is wide. The jaw is very prominent and is quite angular.

If your face is square, your goal is to soften the angles of your face and add length.

Hair: Strive to add fullness on top. A slightly off-center part is best. Wear some hair across the forehead.

Glasses: Wear frames that are slightly rounded to play down the angles of the face. Frames that have some height above the eyes will help to add needed length to the face.

Collars: Collars that are of average to slightly long length will add length to the face. An average to slightly narrow spread will also create the illusion of more length.

MEN'S DIAMOND

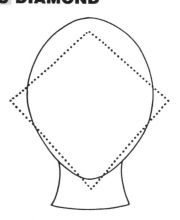

A diamond face is one which is wide at the cheekbones and narrow at the forehead and chin.

If your face is diamond-shaped, your goal is to add width at your forehead and jaw, while making your cheekbones appear narrower.

Hair: Choose a hair style that adds fullness at the forehead and chin. Keep hair close to the face at the cheekbones. Fullness at the back of the neck below the ears will widen the face at the jaw. Sport a high side part and some hair across the forehead.

Glasses: The best frame for you is that which is heavy across the top (adds width at the temples), has straight sides (narrow the cheekbones), and has bottoms that point down and out (widens the appearance of the jaw).

Collars: A collar of average length with an average to slightly wide spread is best for a diamond-shaped face.

MEN'S TRIANGLE or HEART-SHAPED FACE

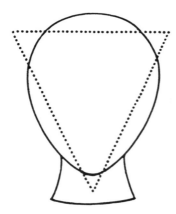

The triangle face is characterized by a wide forehead, high cheek bones, and a tapered chin.

If your face is triangle-shaped, your goal is to add fullness to your chin, at the same time making your forehead appear more narrow.

Hair: Wear your hair close to the temples and the top of the head. A little extra length and fullness in the back will add needed width to the jaw. A strong side part is good, at the same time keeping some hair across the forehead. A beard will also add desired fullness at the chin.

Glasses: Wear slightly curved frames (to diminish the angles). Frames that point down and out will give an illusion of fullness at the jawline. Frames should have an equal thickness all the way around.

Collars: A collar of average length with an average to slightly wide spread is best for a person with a heart or triangle-shaped face.

WOMEN'S OVAL FACE

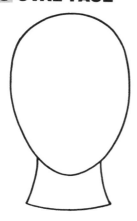

This is the ideal face shape. The width of an oval face is roughly 2/3 of the face length. The forehead is usually slightly wider than the chin, and there is no squareness in the chin.

If your face is oval, your goal is to maintain the natural balance (perfect proportion) of your facial features.

Hair: You can wear almost any hair style, although simple styles are best. Just be sure that you keep your hair in proportion with the rest of you.

Glasses: Choose a frame that preserves the natural balance of the face and is also in proportion to your features and size.

Earrings: You can wear any shape you choose. Just make sure that the size is right for your face. If you have a very petite face, earrings should be no larger than the size of a dime. For an average face – the size of a nickel to a quarter. For a large face wear the size of a quarter to a fifty-cent piece.

WOMEN'S ROUND FACE

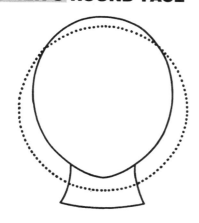

A round face is almost as wide as it is long. It is wide across the cheekbones – a very full face.

If your face is round, your goal is to slim your face and create a longer look, by narrowing your cheekbones and adding width at your forehead and jaw.

Hair: Try to add height to the top of the head, but try to keep all fullness above the ears. By bringing wisps of hair onto your cheeks, your face will lose some of its roundness.

Glasses: Frames should be straight across the top, sides angled in. Avoid extremely round and square styles.

Earrings: Angular earrings are best for you. Square or rectangle earrings will help make your face look more angular. Dangle earrings are good. This will give your face some needed length.

WOMEN'S OBLONG or RECTANGLE FACE

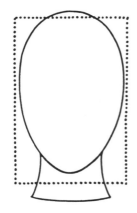

An oblong face is long. The forehead, cheekbones, and jaw all have roughly the same width.

If your face is oblong, your goal is to add width to your face and minimize its length.

Hair: Part hair on the side and wear softly swirled bangs to shorten the face. Adding fullness at the sides will create the illusion of more width. Don't wear a lot of height on top of the head.

Glasses: Frames that are slightly wide and heavy with soft angles will help to focus attention outward (horizontally), breaking the long vertical lines of the face.

Earrings: Shorter, rounder earrings are best for you. You should avoid dangle earrings.

WOMEN'S PEAR FACE

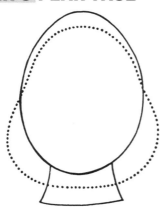

This shape face is characterized by a narrow forehead and wide jawline.

If your face is pear-shaped, your goal is to add fullness at the crown and temples, and to narrow your jaw.

Hair: A short, soft perm is a great way to add height and widen the face at the temples. Keeping some hair on the neck that is visible from the front will soften the jawline. Hair should be kept close to the cheekbones. Also bring some wisps of hair onto the forehead.

Glasses: Frames that are wide at the temple make the upper half of your face appear wider. Choosing a frame that is somewhat heavy across the top is also good for this purpose. Frame bottoms should angle in.

Earrings: Because your face is full at the bottom, earrings that are full at the top are best for you. V-shaped earrings will help fill out the top half of your face.

WOMEN'S SQUARE FACE

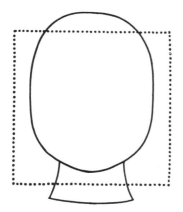

A square face is characterized by a forehead, cheekbones, and jaw that are all about the same width. The face isn't much longer than it is wide. The jaw is very prominent and is quite angular.

If your face is square, your goal is to soften the angles of your face and add length.

Hair: Strive to add fullness on top. A slightly off-center part is best. Your hair should gently hug the jawline. Keeping some hair on the neck that is visible from the front will help to soften the angles of the jaw.

Glasses: Frames that are slightly angular, yet curved at the corners and side pieces, will soften angles.

Earrings: Round earrings are best for you. They will help soften the angles of your face. Also, dangle earrings will give you some needed length.

WOMEN'S DIAMOND FACE

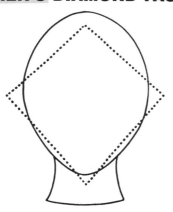

A diamond face is one which is wide at the cheekbones and narrow at the forehead and chin.

If your face is diamond-shaped, your goal is to add width at your forehead and jaw, while making your cheekbones appear narrower.

Hair: Choose a hair style that adds fullness at the forehead and chin. Keep hair close to the face at the cheekbones. Fullness at the back of the neck below the ears will widen the face at the jaw. Wear bangs to add width at the temples.

Glasses: Frames should be straight at the sides and heavy across the top. Bottoms should point down and out.

Earrings: Triangle earrings are best for a diamond face. Rounded earrings are also good. You should avoid square earrings.

WOMEN'S HEART or TRIANGLE-SHAPED FACE

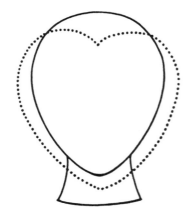

The heart-shaped face is characterized by a wide forehead, high cheek bones, and a tapered chin.

If your face is heart-shaped, your goal is to add fullness to your chin, at the same time making your forehead appear more narrow.

Hair: Wear your hair close to the temples and the top of the head. Curls or fullness at the end of the hair will give the jaw a look of fullness. Soft bangs with a side part will help diminish the width of the forehead.

Glasses: Frames no wider than the temples, and slightly curved are best for you. The bottom of the frames should point down and out. The width of the frame should be widest at the bottom.

Earrings: Triangle earrings are best for you. Rounded earrings are also good. You should avoid square earrings.

SKIN CARE

SKIN CARE: Do you want a beautiful complexion without spending a fortune? The combination of products listed below have helped many of my clients accomplish this after just a few weeks of their use. Many of these people, and also myself, had gone to dermatologists for acne problems for over 15 years without receiving satisfactory results. Then we started on the following regimen. It was after using these products for a few weeks that I received my first compliment ever on my complexion. I hope you enjoy the same benefits.

DAILY:
1. Cleanse the face thoroughly with Cetaphil Lotion. Available in all drug stores.
2. After cleansing, soak a cotton ball with 3% hydrogen peroxide and wipe over oily, acne, and blackhead areas. Caution: Peroxide will lighten hair. Be careful over eyebrows!
3. Moisturize dry or wrinkled areas with Aqualin Original. Available in health food stores, or order direct from manufacturer: Micro Balanced Products (800) 626-7888. Use at night and before applying make-up.

WEEKLY:
1. Slough (remove dead skin cells) skin using a mixture of baking soda and water. Gently scrub the face and rinse.
2. A great facial mask is Milk of Magnesia. Cleanse the face thoroughly and apply Milk of Magnesia generously. Leave on for 15 to 30 minutes, then rinse.

If your skin is oily, you can do the Weekly regimen two or three times a week.

MAKEUP APPLICATION
FOR WOMEN

Makeup, when worn properly, enhances a woman's beauty by bringing out her natural features. It makes her look more alive and energetic. Makeup also protects the skin from wind, sun, pollution, and other elements.

If you don't wear makeup for one reason or another, you really should consider wearing some. Research shows that women who wear makeup earn a salary anywhere from 8 to 20 percent more than women who don't wear any makeup! It doesn't take much time to apply (the following steps can ve done in seven to eight minutes with a little bit of practice), and you will look and feel so much better. This is one definite advantage that women have over men to make themselves look healthier.

Remember to always choose good quality makeup and application brushes. Your overall appearance will be reflected in the quality. Also, don't forget to clean your makeup brushes and sponges once a week with mild soap and water. Your makeup will go on much lighter and easier.

Because your face is a specific shape, your makeup should be applied in a specific way so that you look your very best. The following steps and guidelines will make it simple for you to do so. But remember – practice makes perfect. Give yourself some time to learn proper makeup application.

STEP 1 – UNDER EYE

Apply under-eye concealer to any areas of your face that require a little extra attention – dark circles under the eyes, blemishes, noticeable scars, etc.

STEP 2 – FOUNDATION

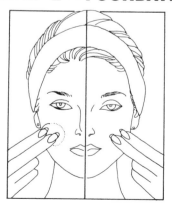

a. Apply foundation with a wet sponge. Start by placing a dot of foundation over each eyebrow, one on each cheek, one on your nose, and one on your chin. Then use the sponge to spread the foundation over your entire face, including your eyelids and lips. Use the sponge in an upward motion – never pull your face down. Blend the foundation at the jawline. You do not need to apply foundation to your neck.

b. If you do have a serious skin flaw that needs a little more attention, apply under-eye concealer to that area of your face once again.

STEP 3 – BLUSH

a. Locate your cheekbone by holding your index finger under your cheekbone, as shown. The contour should be applied directly underneath where your finger lies. Contour slenderizes the face and brings out the cheekbone, making it appear higher. Using a swirling motion, blend the edges. Use the guidelines below to apply contour for your size face.

 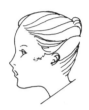 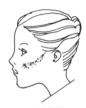

NARROW   **AVERAGE**   **WIDE**

Narrow face – Apply from outer edge of face, blending back toward ear.

Average face – Apply from outer edge of eye to hairline at temple.

Wide face – Apply from the middle of the eye to hairline at temple.

b. Above the line of your finger, apply blush using light feathery strokes, blending it into the hairline at the temple. Do not apply blush under the eye area or below the cheekbone.

STEP 4 – EYEBROWS

The shape of your eyebrows is important in helping your whole face look balanced.

a. **Length** – Lay a pencil or brush along the side of your nose to your tear duct. Remove all hairs on the side of the brush over your nose. Next lay the brush alongside your nose to the outer crease of your eye. Remove all hairs on the outside of the brush.

b. **Shape** – Remove stray hairs under the brow to give your eye a more "open" look. Always remove hairs from the underside of the brow, not the top of the brow. Then, looking straight ahead in a mirror, lay the brush alongside your nose through the center of your pupil. Where the brush crosses your eyebrow should be the arch of your eyebrow.

c. **Pencil** – Fill in your brows lightly as needed, using light, short strokes (as if you are drawing in individual hairs). Use a shade close to your brows' natural coloring. Use a little more pencil if your brows are very thin.

STEP 5 — EYE SHADOW

a. Cover the entire eye area from lid to brow with a light neutral base shadow.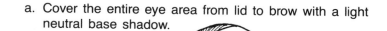

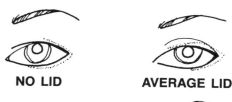

NO LID   **AVERAGE LID**

PROMINENT LID   **ORIENTAL LID**

HOODED LID   **DEEP-SET LID**

b. Determine your eye shape from the following pictures. Then apply eye liner only where the dots are shown on your eye shape. Use a darker neutral color. Smudge the liner to soften the look. (Lining the whole eye makes it appear smaller.)

c. Refer to the pictures to apply eye shadow also. **If your eyes are average, no-lid, or prominent** – apply a medium to dark color eye shadow on the outer third of the eyelid, blending it lightly up toward the brow. Extend shadow along the orbital bone towards the nose (the crease of the eye). **If you have deep-set eyes** – apply a medium to dark color eye shadow just above the crease of your eye. Blend upward and outward around the edge of your eye. **If you have hooded eyes** – apply a medium to dark color eye shadow just above the crease of your eye, widening the color along the "hood." Blend upward and outward toward the eye brow at the edge of your eye. **If you are oriental** – apply a medium to dark color eye shadow where your natural crease would be. Then apply shadow on the outer third of the eyelid, blending it lightly up toward the brow.

STEP 6 — POWDER

a. Use translucent powder only. Do not use colored powder because it will turn darker as the day goes on.

b. Brush across the eye area first, then across the forehead and the rest of the face. Always brush in the same direction as your facial hair grows so that the hair does not stand up.

STEP 7 — LIPSTICK

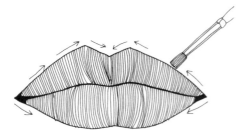

a. With your lips relaxed (mouth naturally closed), outline your lips with a brush or pencil, using a color appropriate for your season. Always work from the outer edge of the lip to the center of the lip. Then fill in the rest of your lips.

b. Blot excess with a tissue. This seals your lipstick, which prevents you from leaving lipstick on a drinking glass.

STEP 8 — MASCARA

Apply mascara to the upper and lower lashes. Then comb the lashes to separate them.

CHAPTER IV
CLOTHING PERSONALITY

The Chinese believe that the world is divided in half by the Yang and Yin personality types – Yang (active and masculine) and Yin (passive and feminine). Most people are a combination of Yang and Yin, but everyone is stronger in one of the personality types. Neither personality type is better than the other, whether you are a man or a woman. You are born with your personality, and it cannont be changed. Yes, you can try to change it, but the change will be temporary, and you will feel awkward and look like you lack self-confidence. Enjoy being yourself!!

Clothing personality revolves around the concept of Yang and Yin. Clothing styles are made to project a type of personality. It is possible that you will fall into two, maybe three different personality types. But we are all mainly one type. Concentrate on your strongest personality type – the one personality that you **really** want to be.

Why is it so important to know your personality type? Clothing styles are made to project a type of personality, and by wearing the styles that fit your personality, you will feel more comfortable and confident.

1. The following test will help you determine whether your personality is more of a Yin or a Yang. **Take the test honestly,** or have someone who can be objective help you. Simply go down the list and read each set of characteristics. Choose the one that **most** describes you and place a check next to it. Do not choose the characteristic that you would **like** to have. Choose what you are. Then, add up the total checks on each side. This will tell you if you are more Yang (active and masculine) or Yin (passive and feminine). Most people have a combination of Yang and Yin traits, but one personality should be dominant.

	DRAMATIC		GAMIN
	NATURAL		INGENUE
	CLASSIC		ROMANTIC

YANG/YIN CHECKLIST

Yang		Yin	
Tall (over 5′6″)	✓	Short (5′6″ and under)	
Large boned	✓	Small boned	
Vivid coloring	✓	Delicate coloring	
Dark hair		Light hair	✓
Formal		Casual	✓
Angular body/face		Rounded body/face	✓
Reserved		Friendly	✓
Aggressive	✓	Shy	
Mature		Youthful	✓
Decisive	✓	Indecisive	
Sophisticated		Natural	✓
Ruddy complexion		Clear complexion	✓
Athletic		Non-athletic	✓
Total Yang	5	Total Yin	8

NOTE: Many people "think" that they are a classic or want to be a classic because they believe it is the only professional and successful business look. **This is not true!** Each personality type has its own successful and professional business look as well as social and casual looks.

2. Now that you know whether you are a Yang or a Yin, you need to figure out which Yang or Yin you are. The following physical features and behavior styles should make it easy for you to decide which personality you are. **Chances are not all of the physical features and behavior styles will be you. It is rare that a person matches the list 100 percent.** Place a check next to your strongest personality.

YANG PERSONALITIES

_____ **DRAMATIC**

Physical features: Slender, angular body/face, striking features, vivid coloring.

Behavior style: Mature, sophisticated, formal, aggressive, creative, enthusiastic, energetic, optimistic, impulsive, stimulating, pre-occupied, theatrical flair.

Needs: Recognition, praise.

Motivators: Recognition, praise, new products, being in the spotlight.

Decision making process: Prefers new alternatives, intuitiveness, boldness.

Approaches taken to succeed: Energy, encouragement, motivation, enthusiasm, establishing rapport, charm.

Time Usage: Busy or pushed, often late, future oriented, over committed, has time for lively and interesting people.

Reaction to tension: Sets goals, starts a new game plan, redirects, verbally attacks, feels anger, walks away from the problem.

Response getters: Personal recognition, flair, ease of effort, image, rapid growth, lead industry.

An example of a dramatic person is Cher Bono. Everything she wears really stands out. Her clothing makes you look twice. Others include: Frank Sinatra, Hammer, Joan Collins, Whitney Houston, Michael Jackson and Arsenio Hall.

_____ **NATURAL**

Physical features: Athletic, relaxed posture, outdoor type, ruddy complexion.

Behavior style: Informal, friendly, open, accepting, warm, casual, down-to-earth, practical, patient, cooperative.

Needs: Popularity, acceptance.

Motivators: Good listener, happy family, harmony, attention, hearing that they have been cooperative.

Decision making process: Prefers to be part of the group's discussion, concerned about the decision's effect on people, likes others to be involved in the decision-making process, idealistic.

Approaches taken to succeed: Acceptance, openness, tolerance, relationships, understanding, flexible, trusting, friendships.

Time usage: Relaxed, has time for everyone, orientation is present, past, future, take things as they come.

Reaction to tension: Creates more harmony, tries to balance feelings, compromises, rationalizes, feels unaccepted.

Response getters: Service, acceptance, teamwork, integrity, satisfied customers, good communication, relationships.

An example of a natural person is Katherine Hepburn. She looks very down to earth all the time; few frills, and yet very vibrant and healthy looking. John Wayne was also a true natural personality type. He loved acting in western films, and he was good at it because of his natural personality. Others include: Sarah Ferguson (Fergie), and Jack Klugman.

_____ CLASSIC

Physical features: Well-proportioned, well-groomed, very tailored, good posture.

Behavior style: Conservative, formal to slightly formal, reserved, precise, careful, sophisticated, dignified, traditional, mature, decisive.

Needs: Security, knowledge.

Motivators: Hearing the fact, carefulness and correctness, reliability, thoroughness and completeness, accomplishment in doing things.

Decision making process: Reluctance, logic, slow, likes to study alternative possibilities in detail, prefers carefully tested alternatives.

Approaches taken to succeed: Carefulness, organization, details, having correct facts.

Time usage: Past oriented, has time for experienced and knowledgeable people.

Reaction to tension: Puts things on paper in a logically correct manner, plans a course of action, withdraws, feels guilt.

Response getters: The bottom line, information, graphs, warranties, images, figures, charts, facts, samples, inventory levels.

An example of a classic person is Larry King - very prim and proper, neat as a pin all the time. Others include: Jerry Seinfeld, Prince Charles, Nancy Reagan, Robert Young, Tony Randall and President George Bush.

YIN PERSONALITIES

_____ GAMIN

Physical features: Small-boned, may have freckles, curly or straight hair in casual style (a mini-natural).

Behavior style: Youthful, energetic, perky, casual, friendly, warm, patient, cooperative, organized, young-at-heart, ambitious, natural.

Needs: Being popular, accepted.

Motivators: Happy family life, good listener, getting along with others, idealistic.

Decision making process: Likes group discussion, concerned about others, idealistic.

Approaches taken to succeed: Candidness, acceptance, patience, relationships, understanding, flexible, believing.

Time usage: Relaxed, in no hurry, spends time in present, past, and future, takes things as they happen.

Reaction to tension: Tries to get along with others, balances feelings, rationalizes, compromises, feels like he doesn't belong.

Response getters: Satisfied customers, service, acceptance, joint efforts, integrity, satisfied customers, good communication, relationships.

An example of a gamin person is Sandy Duncan. She looks right at home in the middle of a wheat field. Others include: Red Buttons, Sara Gilbert, John Denver, Woody Allen and David Letterman.

_____ INGENUE

Physical features: Small-boned, fresh/natural, rounded body/face, beautiful eyes and skin, luxurious hair, delicate coloring (mini-romantic).

Behavior style: Young, sensitive, carefree, sociable, creative, warm, caring.

Needs: Being liked, popularity.

Motivators: Advancement, efficiency, attention, success, competition.

Decision making process: Looks to others for their opinions, concerned about others, idealistic.

Approaches taken to succeed: Efficiency, determination, belief in oneself, task orientation, showing of results.

Time Usage: Keeps promises, has time for people who are efficient, effective, busy, orientation is present, past, and future, has time for intelligent, knowing people.

Reaction to tension: Feels defeated, tries to get along with others, rationalizes, compromises.

Response getters: Succeeding, saving time, image, costs, task, satisfied customers, acceptance, relationships.

An example of an ingenue person is Barbara Eden (I Dream of Jeannie). She's petite, yet looks great in ruffles and chiffons. Others include: Hillary Clinton, Princess Diana, Eddie Fisher, Debbie Reynolds, Michelle Pfeiffer, Dolly Parton and Sammy Davis, Jr.

_____ ROMANTIC

Physical features: Rounded body/face, beautiful eyes and skin, luxurious hair.

Behavior style: Sophisticated, suave, sensual, sensitive, theatrical flair, mature, rich taste, sociable, non-athletic.

Needs: Achievement, making decisions.

Motivators: Results, success, efficiency, the bottom line, a salary increase, promotions, competition.

Decision making process: Realistic, quick, prefers effective alternatives, independent, willing to take a calculated risk.

Approaches taken to succeed: Efficiency, determination, confidence, task orientation, showing of results, punctuality, profit.

Time Usage: Keeps agreements, has time for people who are efficient, present oriented, effective, busy or pushed, orientation is present, past, and future, has time for experienced and knowledgeable people.

Reaction to tension: Changes subordinates, puts on pressure, hires more people, enforces standards, feels like a failure.

Response getters: The bottom line, control, duty, image, winning, costs, time saved, profit margin, task.

An example of a romatic person is Elizabeth Taylor. Her figure and clothing styles spell romance. John Forsythe is another romantic. Just consider his sophisticated, suave and sensual flair. Others include: President Bill Clinton, Linda Evans; Tom Sellack, Tom Cruise and Barbara Bush.

NOTE: You are not limited to the clothing style **pictured** on the page that applies to you. These are only examples. You also will not find every clothing style listed on your page suitable for your body shape. Combine the information in Chapter 3 with the following information to determine your perfect clothing and accessories.

Suits:
  Square shoulders
  Suppressed waist
  Single, double, or no vent
  Two- or three-piece
  Peaked or notched lapels
  Worsted wools, gabardine
  Silk blends
  Bold herringbone
  Large box check, windowpane
  Bold plaid (design, not color)
  Pinstripe – ¼″ to ½″

Shirts – Business/Dress:
  Full or tapered fit
  Broadcloth
  Solids
  Thin stripe (crisp)
  Wide stripe
  Standard, spread, pin collars
  French cuff
  Monograms
  Contrasting collar, cuffs
  Tone-on-tone

Ties:
  Silk – sheen
  Dark solids
  Large-scale patterns
  Stripes – sharp contrast
  Overall geometrics
  Foulard (high contrast)
  Dots

Accessories:
  Collar pin
  Cuff links
  Large watch
  Suspenders
  Pocket square

Dress Shoes:
  Tie, slip-on – plain toe

Topcoat/Trench Coat:
  Fitted or oversized
  Double-breasted
  Belted or unbelted
  Epaulets or plain
  Flannel, fur, fur trim for topcoat

Sport Coats:
  Square shoulders
  Single- or double-breasted
  May be unconstructed
  Smooth or very nubby
  Wool, cotton, silk, blends
  Solids
  Heavy tweeds, houndstooth

Pants:
  Wool, cotton, firm weaves
  Plain or pleated
  Plain or cuffed
  Straight or tapered

Shirts – Casual:
  Broadcloth
  Solids
  Bold plaid
  Bold stripe

Casual Shoes:
  Dressy loafer

Sportswear:
  Costumes (outfits that fit activity)
  Suspenders
  Bulky knit sweaters
  Lounging attire
  Stripes, geometric patterns

DRAMATIC

| CASUAL | SOCIAL | BUSINESS |

Suits:
Natural shoulders
Full-cut
Slightly suppressed waist (if thin)
Single vent
Single-breasted
Two-piece
Flannel, cotton, linen
Tweed, herringbone
Glen plaid
Large box check
Plaid
Subtle chalk stripe

Shirts – Business/Dress:
Medium or full cut
Oxford cloth
Stripes – wide, subtle
Checks
Tattersall
Button-down

Ties:
Silk – matte
Ribbed knit
Heavy wool, linen
Medium-color solids
Medium-scale patterns
Stripes
Foulard
Club, paisley, plaid

Accessories:
Watch with leather band

Dress Shoes:
Tie: cap toe, wing tip
Slip-on: moc toe, wing tip,
tassles and buckles

Topcoat/Trench Coat:
Full cut
Single-breasted
Unbelted
Flannel, tweed for topcoat

Sport Coats:
Natural shoulders
Single-breasted
Nubby textures
Wool, cotton, linen, blends,
corduroy, seersucker
Heavy tweeds
Houndstooth
Plaid
Elbow patches, patch pockets
topstitching

Pants:
Wool, cotton, corduroy, denim
Plain or pleated
Plain or cuffed
Straight or tapered

Shirts – Casual:
Oxford, blends
Stripes – wide
Plaid
Checks

Casual Shoes:
Loafer
Boat shoe
Western boots

Sportswear:
Turtlenecks
Vests
Bulky sweaters
Flannel

NATURAL

CASUAL   SOCIAL   BUSINESS

CLASSIC MEN

Suits:
Slightly padded shoulders
Slightly suppressed waist (or full cut)
Single or double vent
Single-breasted
Two- or three-piece
Worsted, flannel, cotton, blends
Solids, tweed, herringbone, small box check,
windowpane, glen plaid, chalk stripe,
pin stripe – ⅛″ to ¼″, woven-in designs

Shirts – Business/Dress:
Medium range fit
Oxford or broadcloth
Solids
Subtle or crisp stripes
Tattersall
Button-down, standard, or pin
Contrasting collar and cuffs
Monograms

Ties:
Silk – sheen, matte
Wool – smooth
Linen
Medium to dark solids
Medium-scale patterns
Stripes
Foulard – rounded, geometric
Club, dots

Accessories:
Watch – metal or leather band
Pocket square

Dress Shoes:
Tie: plain toe, wing tip, cap toe
Slip-on: plain toe, wing tip, moc toe

Topcoat/Trench Coat:
Full cut or fitted
Single- or double-breasted
Belted or unbelted
Flannel, tweed for topcoat

Sport Coats:
Slightly padded or natural shoulders
Single- or double-breasted
Smooth textures
Solids, woven-in designs, subtle tweed,
plaid, houndstooth

Pants:
Wool, cotton, corduroy (stiff)
Plain or cuffed
Straight legs

Shirts – Casual:
Oxford, blends
Solids
Tattersall
Button-down

Casual Shoes:
Loafer
Boat shoe

Sportswear:
Polo shirts
Plaid pants
Nautical motifs

CLASSIC

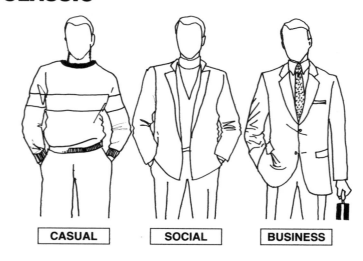

| CASUAL | SOCIAL | BUSINESS |

Suits:
Slightly padded shoulders
Slightly suppressed waist
Single vent
Single-breasted
Two-piece
Worsted, cotton, blends, gabardine
Solids, tweed, herringbone, small box check,
glen plaid, 1/8″ pin stripe, woven-in designs

Shirts – Business/Dress:
Medium range fit
Broadcloth
Solids
Thin, crisp stripes
Checks, tattersall
Standard, button-down, round

Ties:
Silk – matte, slight sheen
Ribbed knit
Wool – smooth
Linen
Bow ties
Medium-color solids
Small-scale patterns
Stripes – sharp and/or colorful
Foulard
Club, plaid

Accessories:
Watch – leather band
Suspenders

Dress Shoes:
Tie: cap toe, plain toe
Slip-on: moc toe, tassles and buckles

Topcoat/Trench Coat:
Fitted
Single-breasted
Unbelted
Flannel for topcoat

Sport Coats:
Slightly padded shoulders
Single-breasted
Wool, cotton, linen, corduroy
Smooth to slightly nubby
Solids
Subtle tweed
Seersucker
Small plaid
Topstitching, patch pockets

Pants:
Cotton, wool, gabardine, corduroy, denim
Pleated or plain
Straight leg

Shirts – Casual:
Broadcloth, oxford, blends
Solids
Checks
Tattersall
Stripe
Plaid

Casual Shoes:
Loafer
Boat shoe
Saddle oxford

Sportswear:
Sweater vest
Argyle patterns

GAMIN

CASUAL   SOCIAL   BUSINESS

INGENUE MEN

Suits:
Slightly padded shoulders
Suppressed waist
Double or no vent
Single-breasted
Two-piece
Soft wools, silks, blends
Solids
Subtle stripes
Woven-in designs

Shirts – Business/Dress:
Tapered fit, French cuffs
Broadcloth, silk
Solids
Stripe – subtle, blended
Checks, tattersall
Standard, pin, or rounded collar
Monograms

Ties:
Silk – sheen
Crepe
Solids
Medium-scale patterns
Stripes
Foulard
Paisley – soft, blended

Accessories:
Cuff links
Rings
Slim-line watch
Pocket square

Dress Shoes:
Slip-on: plain toe
Tie: plain toe

Topcoat/Trench Coat:
Fitted
Single-breasted
Belted, epaulets
Cashmere, fur, leather for topcoats

Sport Coats:
Square or natural shoulders
May be unconstructed
Single-breasted
Smooth textures
Wool, silk, blends, leather
Solids, woven-in designs

Pants:
Corduroy, leather
Pleated or plain
Tapered

Shirts – Casual:
Silk
Solids
Unusual collars

Casual Shoes:
Italian boot
Dressy loafer

Sportswear:
Italian styling
Short, fitted jackets
Velour warm-ups
Soft sweaters

INGENUE

CASUAL   SOCIAL   BUSINESS

ROMANTIC MEN

Suits:
Padded shoulders
Suppressed waist
Double or no vent
Single- or double-breasted
Two-piece
Soft wools, silks, blends
Solids
Subtle stripes
Woven-in designs

Shirts – Business/Dress:
Tapered fit, French cuffs
Broadcloth, silk
Solids
Stripe – subtle, blended
Standard, pin, or rounded collars
Monograms

Ties:
Silk – sheen
Crepe
Solids
Medium-scale patterns
Stripes
Foulard
Paisley – soft, blended

Accessories:
Cuff links
Rings
Slim-line watch
Pocket square

Dress Shoes:
Slip-on: plain toe
Tie: plain toe

Topcoat/Trench Coat:
Fitted
Single- or double-breasted
Belted, epaulets
Cashmere, fur, leather for topcoats

Sport Coats:
Square or natural shoulders
May be unconstructed
Single- or double-breasted
Smooth textures
Wool, silk, blends, leather
Solids, woven-in designs

Pants:
Corduroy, leather
Pleated or plain
Tapered

Shirts – Casual:
Silk
Solids
Unusual collars

Casual Shoes:
Italian boot
Dressy loafer

Sportswear:
Italian styling
Short, fitted jackets
Velour warm-ups
Soft sweaters

ROMANTIC

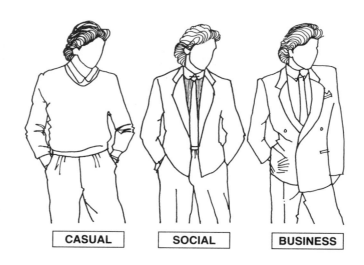

CASUAL   SOCIAL   BUSINESS

DRAMATIC WOMEN

Clothing:

Bold contrasts of color
Severely plain necklines
Large, plain areas with little detail
Widely spaced designs
Emphasis at waist; for example, wide belts
Angular, bold, severe, and long unbroken lines
Extreme exaggerations

Prints: Plain or bold, abstract, geometric

Fabrics: Nubby weaves, satin, very shiny, lustrous, metallic, easy drape, firm weaves, heavy

Shoes: Designer; high heels to flats, all colors

Jewelry: Plain, bold, ornate, elaborate, larger in size

Hair: Extremes of style, stays with fashion

Makeup: Medium to heavy, very theatrical

DRAMATIC

| CASUAL | SOCIAL | BUSINESS |

Clothing:

Casual chic
Lots of texture
Clothing never tight or full
A-line, straight, or wrap-around skirts
Simple detail

Prints: Plaids, checks, stripes, plain

Fabrics: Rough linen and matte finish, raw silk, tweed, flannel, jersey, gabardine, heavy crepe

Shoes: Plain pumps, low heels, neutral colors

Jewelry: Plain, simple, smaller in size

Hair: Casual, natural, curly or straight, easy to care for

Makeup: Light, very natural

NATURAL

| CASUAL | SOCIAL | BUSINESS |

Clothing:

> Soft pleats or folds
> Simple skirts
> Small details, belts, buttons
> Simple lines
> Softly tailored necklines
> Clean, straight lines

Prints: Small evenly spaced stripes, small polka dots, small geometric designs, small evenly spaced paisleys

Fabrics: Cotton or cotton blends, silk, wool flannel, wool crepe, cotton jersey, cashmere

Shoes: Plain pumps, high to low heels, neutral colors

Jewelry: Average size, conservative, rich/simple looking; e.g., pearls

Hair: Simple, neat, plain, but not too stiff

Makeup: Light to medium

CLASSIC

CASUAL **SOCIAL** **BUSINESS**

Clothing:

Casual
Youthful
Bright colors
Small details: Buttons, bows, pockets
Short jackets

Prints: Checks, small plaids, stripes

Fabrics: Cottons, jersey, corduroy, flannel, soft tweeds, velveteen

Shoes: Low heels, neutral colors

Jewelry: Minimal, small, simple

Hair: Short, natural, curly or straight, casual, easy to care for

Makeup: Light, very natural

GAMIN

| CASUAL | SOCIAL | BUSINESS |

Clothing:

> Curvy details and lines
> Gathers
> Youthful
> Bouffant sleeves
> Eyelet and lace trims
> Silhouettes: Bouffant, princess, or empire

> **Prints:** Small polka dots, flowers, lace

> **Fabrics:** Georgette, cotton, angora, soft woolens, lace, fabrics soft to touch

> **Shoes:** Medium to low heels with details, all colors

Jewelry: Dainty, detailed; e.g., pearls, cameos, feminine

Hair: Soft, curly or wavy, feminine

Makeup: Light

INGENUE

| CASUAL | SOCIAL | BUSINESS |

Clothing:

Very feminine
Restrained curves
Silhouettes: Bouffant, crisp, or softly draped
Emphasis above waist
Fitted waistline
Softly tailored

Prints: Polka dots, soft prints, flowers, lace

Fabrics: Silk, chiffon, angora, soft wool, satin, fine jersey, velvet, lace, fabrics soft to touch

Shoes: High heels with details, all colors

Jewelry: Elegant but lavish, feminine

Hair: Soft, curly or wavy, feminine

Makeup: Medium to heavy

ROMANTIC

CASUAL **SOCIAL** **BUSINESS**

It is possible that you may be a disbeliever, one who doesn't think this clothing is right for you. You may like the styles but not think they're right for you and therefore you have never tried them. Do yourself a favor – go to the store, try these styles on, and have a sales clerk or objective friend or relative tell you how they look.

Take this book shopping with you. The best look for you is contained within the pages of this book. The information is invaluable.

It is likely that all clothing styles listed under your personality will not be right for you. You need to combine the information here with the information you recorded in Chapter 3 (Body Architecture - the clothing charts) to succeed at finding your best look.

If your body changes - if you gain or lose weight, for example - your personality has not changed. You simply go back to the clothing charts and reassess your proportioned and mis-proportioned figure spots. This information will help you for the rest of your life.

CHAPTER V
WARDROBE PLANNING

Do you approach your closet in the morning with a smile on your face, saying to yourself, "What do I get to wear today?!" Or do you say with a frown, "What can I wear today?" Do you feel that you have just one or two outfits that you feel terrific in, and feel that you'll have a lucky day when you wear them? That is the way you should feel about all of your clothing! If you do not feel that everything you wear is lucky or is a power piece, get rid of those clothes. This does not make you a wasteful person. If you do not feel strong and successful all day everyday, you can not and will not be a successful person. Remember – you create your own success!

It is easy to perceive a successful business person simply by seeing him. His handsomely tailored, quality suit speaks for itself. What you see is what he is – professional, successful, confident, intelligent.

First impressions are very important. Remember, you only have one chance to make a good first impression. More often than not, a lasting impression stems from that first impression. Everything that you wear sends out a visual message to the people whom you deal with every day. Therefore, it is very important that you send out the most positive message possible.

It is easy to become lax in our appearance. A business man sometimes forgets that all many people know about him is what they see. When meeting a person for the first time, in those first few seconds the person evaluates him on his professionalism, his success, his education, his social status, and many other points.

People who are well-dressed and well-groomed earn more, are promoted faster, and are perceived as more competent than those who are not. Everything that you wear makes a statement about you. Since you are making a statement, you should send the best possible message all the time.

This chapter contains points of dressing. It also contains an achievement dressing plan. To put your achievement dressing plan to work for you, you must first analyze your existing wardrobe. The next few pages, "Successful Checklist" is included for both men and women.

FOURTEEN POINTS OF DRESSING
FOR MEN

OVER 14 – OVERDRESSED   **UNDER 8 – UNDERDRESSED**

POINTS	ITEMS
1	Each color (count only dominate colors)
1	Bow
1	Tie
1	Buttons (contrasting: 1 each)
1	Belt
1	Every piece of jewelry
1	Red hair
1	Colored socks
	(only if socks are different color than pants or shoes)
1	Briefcase
1	Shoes, plus following:
1	Detail on shoes

Every morning, look at yourself in a full length mirror and count the number of points that you are wearing. Under 8 points is considered underdressed (not wearing enough color or accessories to look interesting). Over 14 points is considered overdressed (wearing too much color or too many accessories). If you are dressing for business, you should have between 8 and 10 points. Simple is sophisticated, but keep it interesting!

SUCCESSFUL WARDROBE CHECKLIST

Successful Wardrobe Checklist for Men

The foundation for your new wardrobe should be good quality pieces of clothing in your best neutral colors. It includes the pieces of clothing that you should own for a wardrobe for all occasions. The amount of clothing suggested here is enough to begin with, as it will give you several different looks for any situation. To this wardrobe you can add other pieces of clothing and accessories as you have the money to spend. (See the last page of the checklist for your total wardrobe needs.)

Take the time to check off the pieces of clothing that you currently have so that you will easily know what you need to purchase later.

COOL
WEATHER ☐

WARM
WEATHER ☐

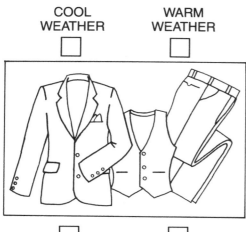

Suits – Solid neutral color; two- or three-piece; conservative cut (something that will not go out of style). For cool weather, a dark wool or wool blend is good. For warm weather, a medium or dark light-weight wool, wool blend, or cotton blend is appropriate.

☐   ☐

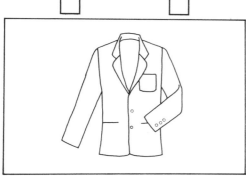

Sport Coats – Solid color; basic style. For cool weather, a wool, wool blend, or suede. For warm weather, a wool blend, cotton blend, or other good-looking light fabric.

☐   ☐

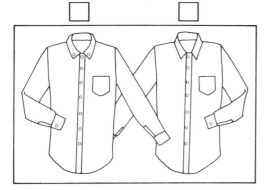

Business Shirts – Solid color. Oxford cloth or broadcloth; button-down or standard collar.

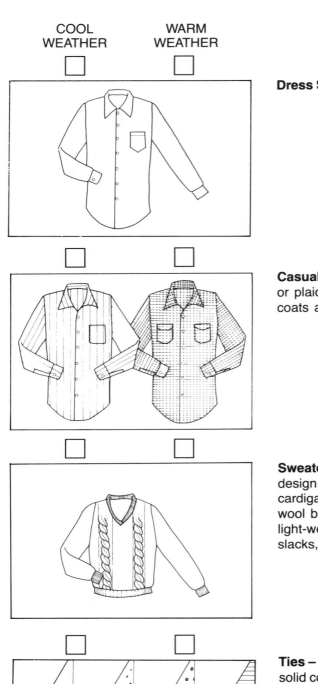

COOL
WEATHER

WARM
WEATHER

Dress Shirts – Solid color. Broadcloth with a standard collar.

Casual Shirts – Either a solid color or a mild stripe, check, or plaid. These shirts should also work well with your sport coats and slacks.

Sweaters – A basic or neutral color, possibly with a light design in the sweater. Styles that work well are V-neck, cardigan, and crew neck. For cool weather, choose a wool or wool blend. For warm weather, choose cotton knit or light-weight wool. These should coordinate with your dress slacks, shirts, and casual slacks.

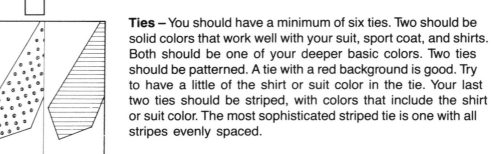

Ties – You should have a minimum of six ties. Two should be solid colors that work well with your suit, sport coat, and shirts. Both should be one of your deeper basic colors. Two ties should be patterned. A tie with a red background is good. Try to have a little of the shirt or suit color in the tie. Your last two ties should be striped, with colors that include the shirt or suit color. The most sophisticated striped tie is one with all stripes evenly spaced.

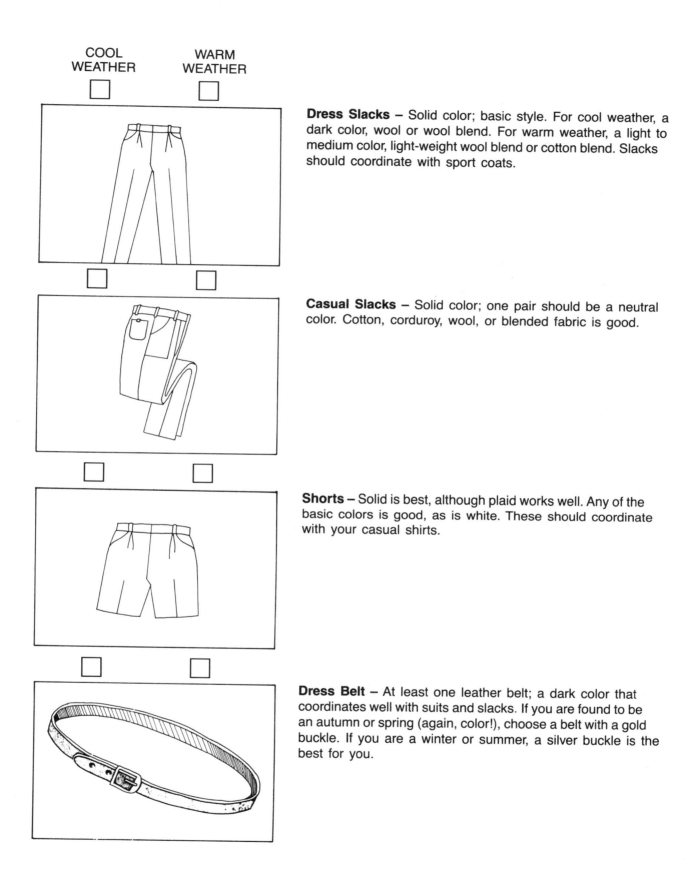

Dress Slacks – Solid color; basic style. For cool weather, a dark color, wool or wool blend. For warm weather, a light to medium color, light-weight wool blend or cotton blend. Slacks should coordinate with sport coats.

Casual Slacks – Solid color; one pair should be a neutral color. Cotton, corduroy, wool, or blended fabric is good.

Shorts – Solid is best, although plaid works well. Any of the basic colors is good, as is white. These should coordinate with your casual shirts.

Dress Belt – At least one leather belt; a dark color that coordinates well with suits and slacks. If you are found to be an autumn or spring (again, color!), choose a belt with a gold buckle. If you are a winter or summer, a silver buckle is the best for you.

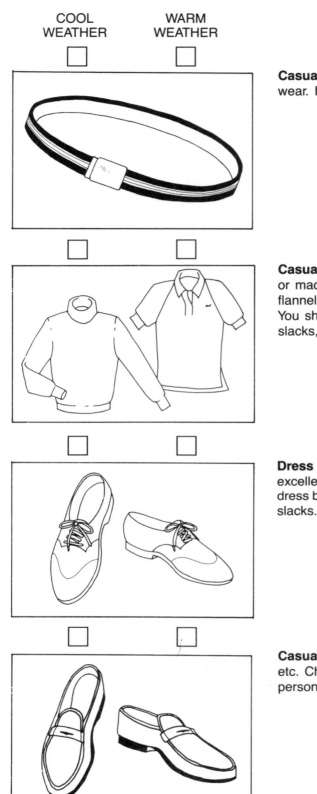

Casual Belt – A leather or fabric belt is appropriate for casual wear. It should be a plain color or striped.

Casual Shirts – For warm weather, short-sleeved polo shirts or madras shirts are good choices. For cooler weather, a flannel shirt, turtleneck, or long-sleeved polo shirt looks nice. You should have several casual shirts to coordinate with slacks, shorts, and sweaters.

Dress Shoes – A leather dressy loafer or laced oxford are excellent choices. Choose a neutral color that matches your dress belt. The color should also coordinate with the suit and slacks.

Casual Shoes – Loafers, casual laced shoes, tennis shoes, etc. Choose a pair of shoes (or boots) that match your personality.

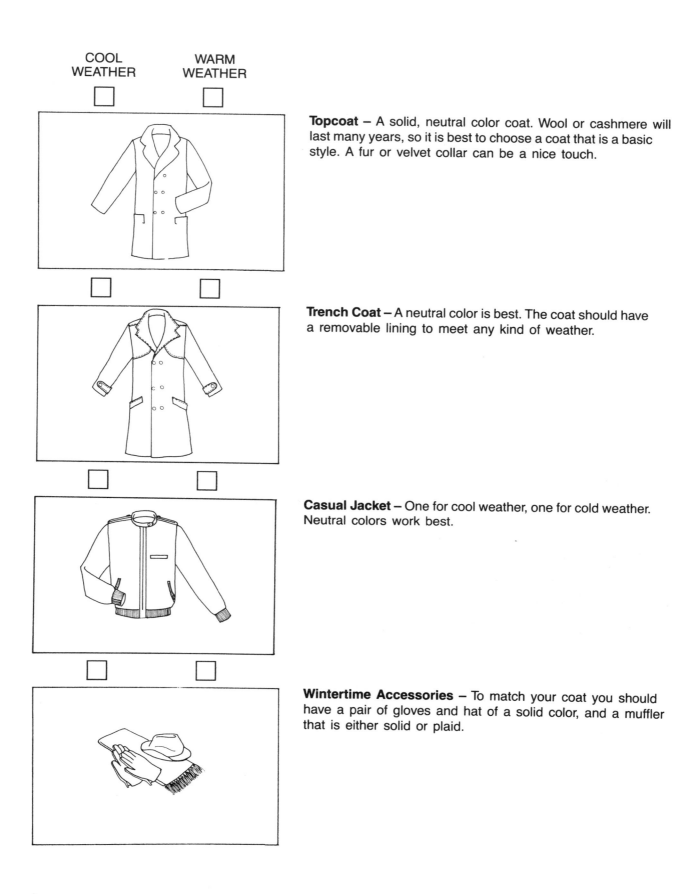

Topcoat – A solid, neutral color coat. Wool or cashmere will last many years, so it is best to choose a coat that is a basic style. A fur or velvet collar can be a nice touch.

Trench Coat – A neutral color is best. The coat should have a removable lining to meet any kind of weather.

Casual Jacket – One for cool weather, one for cold weather. Neutral colors work best.

Wintertime Accessories – To match your coat you should have a pair of gloves and hat of a solid color, and a muffler that is either solid or plaid.

COOL
WEATHER

WARM
WEATHER

Sports Wear – Whether you play tennis, golf, or swim, you should have the appropriate clothing for your sport.

Personal Items – Underwear, pajamas, robe, slippers.

Formal Wear – If your lifestyle dictates, a tuxedo should be part of your wardrobe. Make sure that its color is appropriate for you.

Accessories – Leather briefcase, umbrella, handkerchief.

Once you have these basic articles of clothing, you will be ready to expand your wardrobe. By buying items in neutral and basic colors, and by purchasing more solids than patterns, you will get the most variety of outfits from the fewest items of clothing. The following is a list of clothing items that you should add to your wardrobe as your budget permits. Combined with the clothing listed above, your wardrobe will be large enough and have enough variety that you won't need to buy more clothing unless you want to.

The Corporate Wardrobe

8 suits (3 solids)
2 sport coats
2 dress slacks
12 dress shirts
15 ties
2 casual slacks
4 casual shirts
4 pair dress shoes
2 pair casual shoes

The Non-Corporate Wardrobe

1 suit (solid)
2 sport coats
2 dress slacks
6 dress shirts
6 ties
6 casual slacks
12 casual shirts
2 pair dress shoes
3 pair casual shoes

The corporate wardrobe is for the man who has a job or works in an office which dictates a professional look. For example, if you work in a bank, the corporate wardrobe is for you. If you are a salesperson or have a job that puts you in the eyes of the clients, the corporate wardrobe is appropriate.

The non-corporate wardrobe is for the man who has a more casual job or works in a more casual atmosphere. For example, if you are a carpenter, the non-corporate wardrobe will probably meet your clothing needs.

The appropriate wardrobe for you can usually be determined simply by noticing what other employees wear on the job, especially the employees you consider successful. Caution, however, that some employees may be "under-dressed" while others are "over-dressed." You must assess the properly dressed people.

If you develop a "shadow" as the day goes on, keep extra shaving equipment at the office to get rid of this unkempt look.

After you have applied aftershave or cologne, wash your hands. Otherwise, each time you shake hands with someone, that person will go away smelling like you.

Keep your fingernails clean and well trimmed.

Keep any hair in your nose and ears trimmed.

It is a good idea to keep an extra shirt and tie at the office. You never know when you might spill something on yourself, your car may break down on the way to work, or other little disasters may happen.

Comments about personal grooming:

NOTE: _____

_____

General Rules for Combining Suit/Shirt/Tie

1. When choosing your suit, shirt, and tie for the day, combine three solids, two solids and one pattern, or one solid and two non-competing patterns. Unless you work in the fashion industry and know what you are doing, do not combine three patterns. It is very difficult to do and achieve a good look. The look usually ends up being too busy and distracting.

2. Strive for contrast. When all pieces of clothing are the same color, the overall look can be very dull. Choosing a tie whose color contrasts with that of the suit will make a world of difference.

3. Combine compatible fabrics. For example, you should never wear a hairy wool tie with a linen jacket, or vice versa. Make sure that you are wearing an outfit, not just **pieces**.

4. Don't mix styles of clothing. For example, don't wear a suit coat with casual pants.

The following chart will help you properly combine patterns. Here are two examples that will help you understand how to use them.

Say you are going to wear a herringbone suit. If you wear a solid tie with it, you can wear a solid, striped, plaid, or tattersall shirt. If you wear any other style tie, you should only wear a solid shirt.

A second example: A plaid tie should never be worn with a striped, glen plaid, or bold plaid suit. If worn with a solid suit, it can be worn with a solid or tattersall shirt. It should only be worn with a solid shirt with any other style shirt.

COMBINING
SUIT/SHIRT/TIE

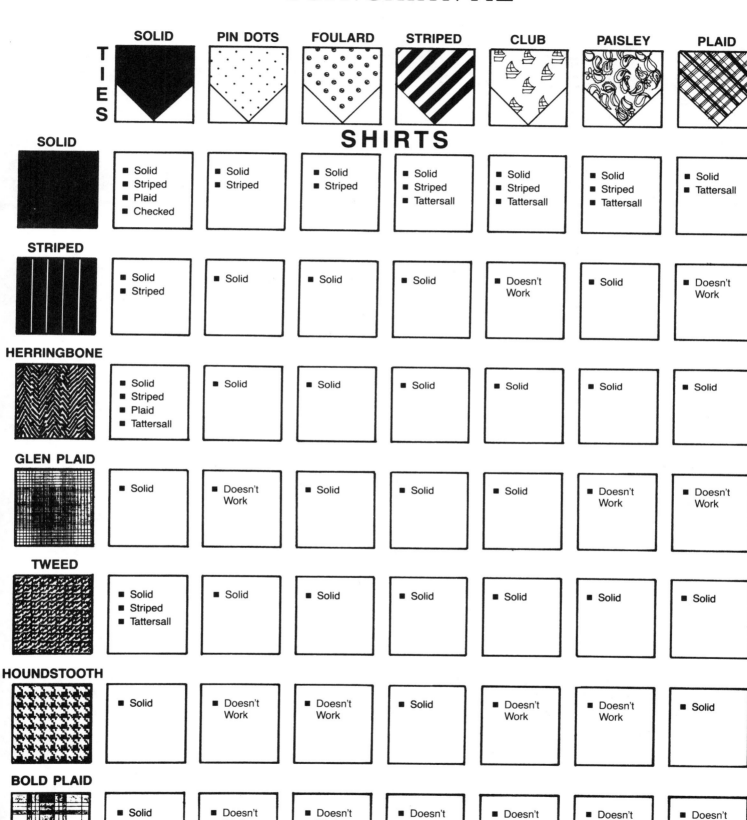

	SOLID	PIN DOTS	FOULARD	STRIPED	CLUB	PAISLEY	PLAID
SHIRTS							
SOLID	■ Solid ■ Striped ■ Plaid ■ Checked	■ Solid ■ Striped	■ Solid ■ Striped	■ Solid ■ Striped ■ Tattersall	■ Solid ■ Striped ■ Tattersall	■ Solid ■ Striped ■ Tattersall	■ Solid ■ Tattersall
STRIPED	■ Solid ■ Striped	■ Solid	■ Solid	■ Solid	■ Doesn't Work	■ Solid	■ Doesn't Work
HERRINGBONE	■ Solid ■ Striped ■ Plaid ■ Tattersall	■ Solid	■ Solid	■ Solid	■ Solid	■ Solid	■ Solid
GLEN PLAID	■ Solid	■ Doesn't Work	■ Solid	■ Solid	■ Solid	■ Doesn't Work	■ Doesn't Work
TWEED	■ Solid ■ Striped ■ Tattersall	■ Solid	■ Solid	■ Solid	■ Solid	■ Solid	■ Solid
HOUNDSTOOTH	■ Solid	■ Doesn't Work	■ Doesn't Work	■ Solid	■ Doesn't Work	■ Doesn't Work	■ Solid
BOLD PLAID	■ Solid	■ Doesn't Work	■ Doesn't Work	■ Doesn't Work	■ Doesn't Work	■ Doesn't Work	■ Doesn't Work

87

FOURTEEN POINTS OF DRESSING
FOR WOMEN

OVER 14 – OVERDRESSED   UNDER 8 – UNDERDRESSED

POINTS	ITEMS
1	Each color (count only dominate colors)
1	Each: bow, ruffle, flounce
1	Each: scarf, flower, tie
1	Buttons (contrasting: 1 each)
1	Belt
1	Every piece of jewelry
1	Nail polish
1	Red hair
1	Colored hose or socks (only if hose or socks are different color than skirt or pants or shoes)
1	Briefcase, purse
1	Shoes, plus following:
1	Detail on shoes
1	Open toe on shoes
1	Sling on shoes
1	Nail polish on toes (if visible with shoes on)

Every morning, look at yourself in a full length mirror and count the number of points that you are wearing. Under 8 points is considered underdressed (not wearing enough color or accessories to look interesting). Over 14 points is considered overdressed (wearing too much color or too many accessories). If you are dressing for business, you should have between 10 and 12 points. Simple is sophisticated, but keep it interesting!

SUCCESSFUL WARDROBE CHECKLIST

Successful Wardrobe Checklist for Women

The foundation for your new wardrobe should be good quality pieces of clothing in your best neutral colors. It includes the pieces of clothing that you should own for a wardrobe for all occasions. The amount of clothing suggested here is enough to begin with, as it will give you several different looks for any situation. To this wardrobe you can add other pieces of clothing and accessories as you have the money to spend. (See the last page of the checklist for your total wardrobe needs.)

Take the time to check off the pieces of clothing that you currently have so that you will easily know what you need to purchase later.

COOL
WEATHER

WARM
WEATHER

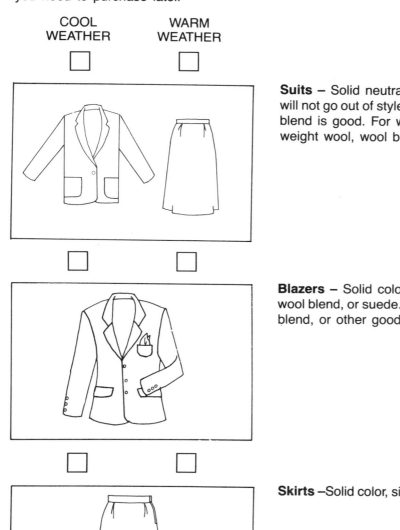

Suits – Solid neutral color; conservative cut (something that will not go out of style). For cool weather, a dark wool or wool blend is good. For warm weather, a medium or dark light-weight wool, wool blend, or cotton blend is appropriate.

Blazers – Solid color; basic style. For cool weather, a wool, wool blend, or suede. For warm weather, a wool blend, cotton blend, or other good-looking light fabric.

Skirts –Solid color, simple style. Must coordinate with blazers.

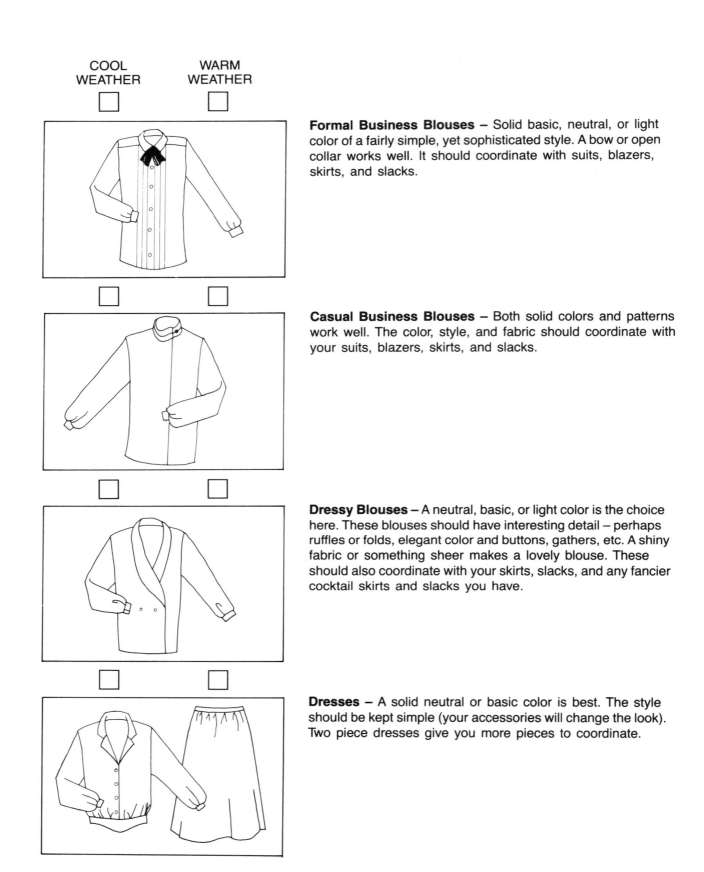

COOL
WEATHER □

WARM
WEATHER □

Formal Business Blouses – Solid basic, neutral, or light color of a fairly simple, yet sophisticated style. A bow or open collar works well. It should coordinate with suits, blazers, skirts, and slacks.

□ □

Casual Business Blouses – Both solid colors and patterns work well. The color, style, and fabric should coordinate with your suits, blazers, skirts, and slacks.

□ □

Dressy Blouses – A neutral, basic, or light color is the choice here. These blouses should have interesting detail – perhaps ruffles or folds, elegant color and buttons, gathers, etc. A shiny fabric or something sheer makes a lovely blouse. These should also coordinate with your skirts, slacks, and any fancier cocktail skirts and slacks you have.

□ □

Dresses – A solid neutral or basic color is best. The style should be kept simple (your accessories will change the look). Two piece dresses give you more pieces to coordinate.

90

COOL
WEATHER ☐

WARM
WEATHER ☐

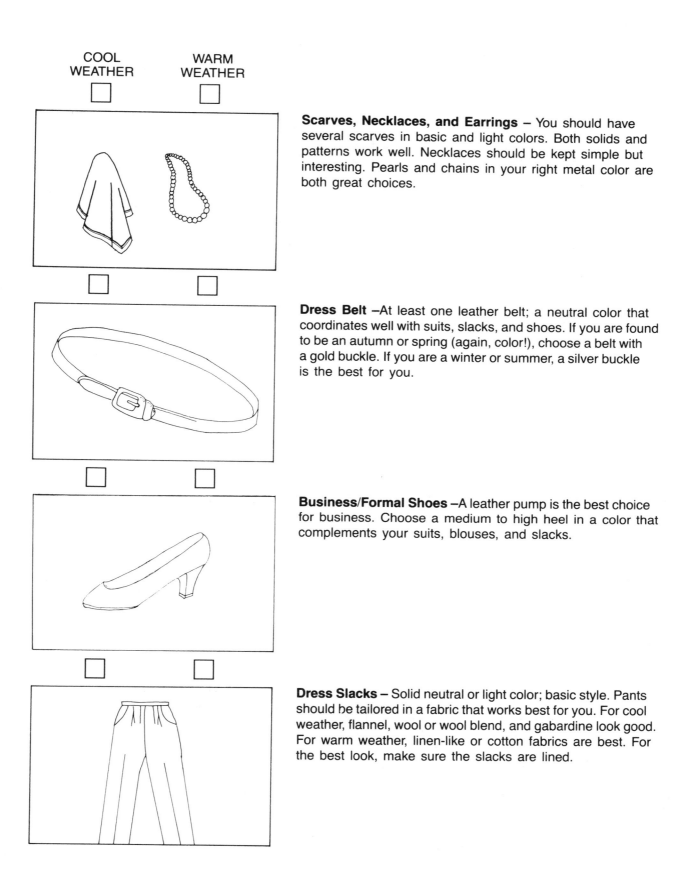

☐ ☐

Scarves, Necklaces, and Earrings – You should have several scarves in basic and light colors. Both solids and patterns work well. Necklaces should be kept simple but interesting. Pearls and chains in your right metal color are both great choices.

☐ ☐

Dress Belt –At least one leather belt; a neutral color that coordinates well with suits, slacks, and shoes. If you are found to be an autumn or spring (again, color!), choose a belt with a gold buckle. If you are a winter or summer, a silver buckle is the best for you.

☐ ☐

Business/Formal Shoes –A leather pump is the best choice for business. Choose a medium to high heel in a color that complements your suits, blouses, and slacks.

☐ ☐

Dress Slacks – Solid neutral or light color; basic style. Pants should be tailored in a fabric that works best for you. For cool weather, flannel, wool or wool blend, and gabardine look good. For warm weather, linen-like or cotton fabrics are best. For the best look, make sure the slacks are lined.

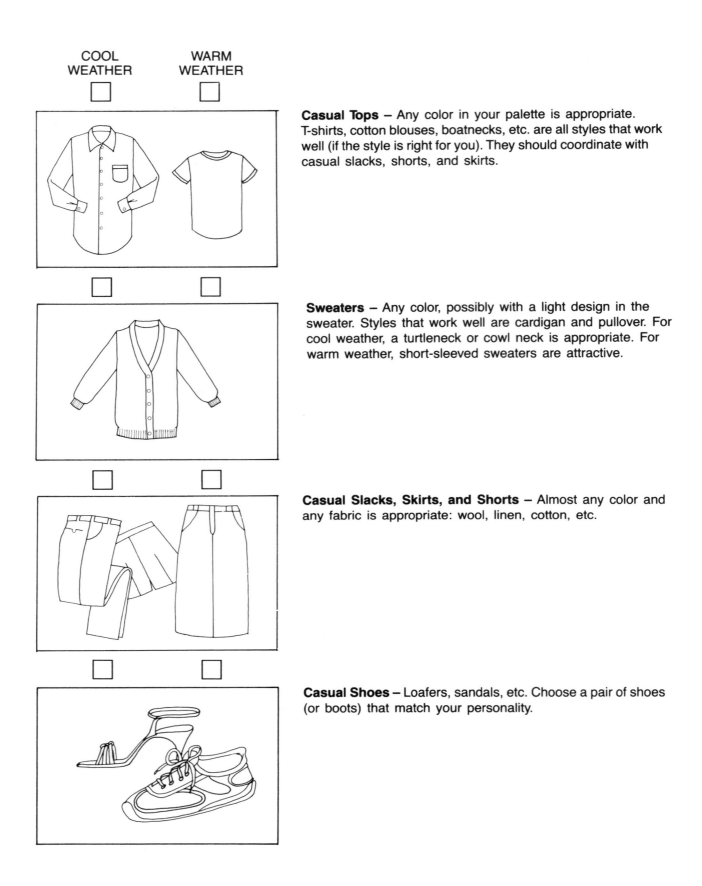

Casual Tops – Any color in your palette is appropriate. T-shirts, cotton blouses, boatnecks, etc. are all styles that work well (if the style is right for you). They should coordinate with casual slacks, shorts, and skirts.

Sweaters – Any color, possibly with a light design in the sweater. Styles that work well are cardigan and pullover. For cool weather, a turtleneck or cowl neck is appropriate. For warm weather, short-sleeved sweaters are attractive.

Casual Slacks, Skirts, and Shorts – Almost any color and any fabric is appropriate: wool, linen, cotton, etc.

Casual Shoes – Loafers, sandals, etc. Choose a pair of shoes (or boots) that match your personality.

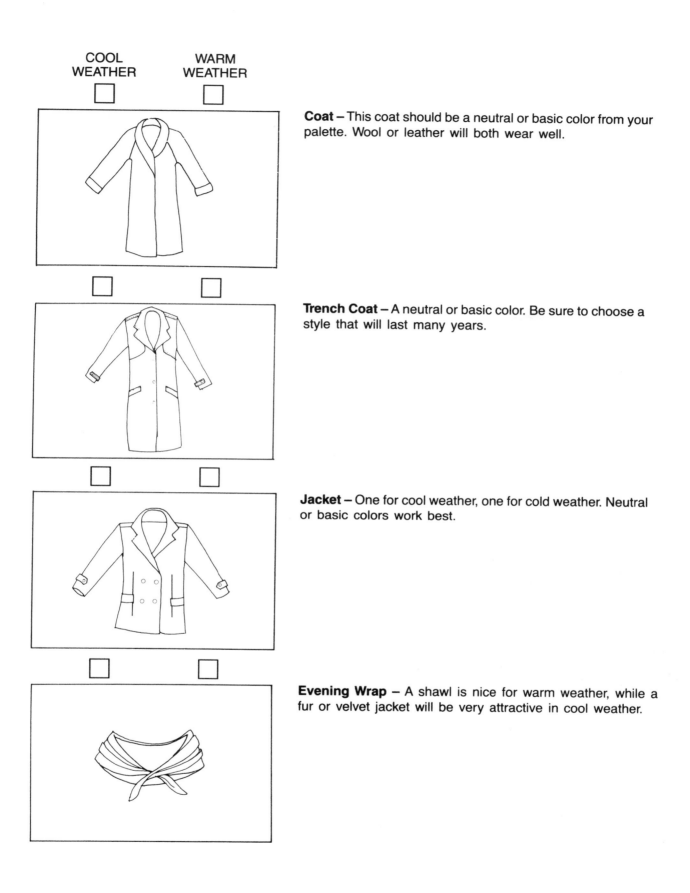

COOL
WEATHER ☐

WARM
WEATHER ☐

Coat – This coat should be a neutral or basic color from your palette. Wool or leather will both wear well.

☐ ☐

Trench Coat – A neutral or basic color. Be sure to choose a style that will last many years.

☐ ☐

Jacket – One for cool weather, one for cold weather. Neutral or basic colors work best.

☐ ☐

Evening Wrap – A shawl is nice for warm weather, while a fur or velvet jacket will be very attractive in cool weather.

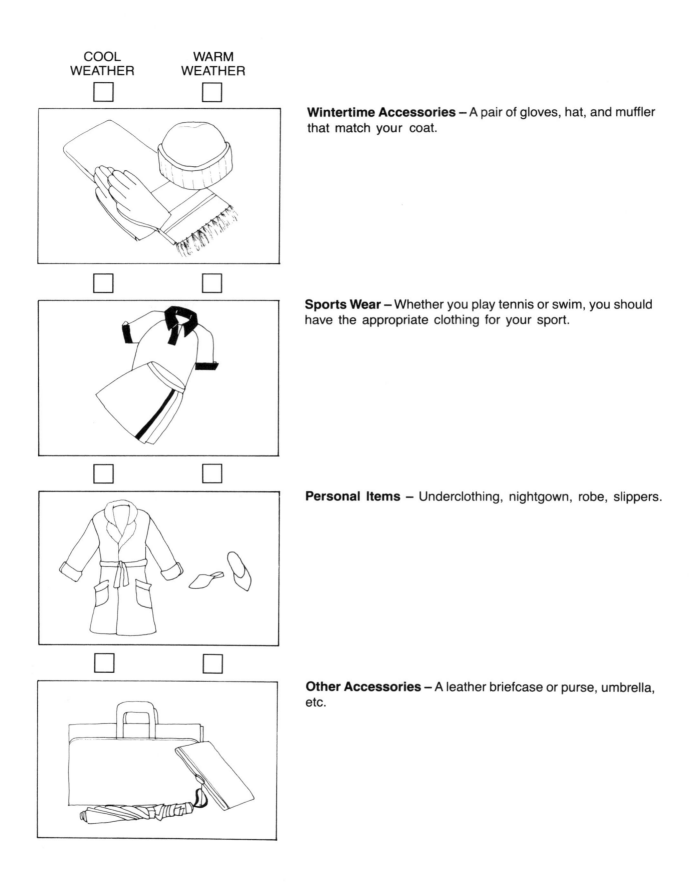

COOL
WEATHER ☐   WARM
WEATHER ☐

☐   ☐

☐   ☐

☐   ☐

Wintertime Accessories – A pair of gloves, hat, and muffler that match your coat.

Sports Wear – Whether you play tennis or swim, you should have the appropriate clothing for your sport.

Personal Items – Underclothing, nightgown, robe, slippers.

Other Accessories – A leather briefcase or purse, umbrella, etc.

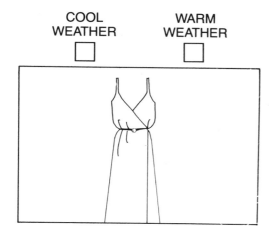

COOL
WEATHER ☐

WARM
WEATHER ☐

Cocktail/Formal Wear – For evenings out you should have a cocktail dress, evening gown, pants, or skirt. Any color, style, or fabric that fits your personality type is appropriate.

Once you have these basic articles of clothing, you will be ready to expand your wardrobe. By buying items in neutral and basic colors, and by purchasing more solids than patterns, you will get the most variety of outfits from the fewest items of clothing. The following is a list of clothing items that you should add to your wardrobe as your budget permits. Combined with the clothing listed above, your wardrobe will be large enough and have enough variety that you won't need to buy more clothing unless you want to.

The Corporate Wardrobe

5 suits (3 solids)
2 business/dress blazers
3 business/dress skirts
2 dress pants
6 business/dress blouses
4 business/dress dresses
4 pair dress shoes
2 informal pants or skirts
6 informal tops
2 pair casual shoes

The Non-Corporate Wardrobe

1 suit (solid)
2 blazers
2 formal daytime skirts
2 dress pants
6 formal daytime blouses
2 formal daytime dresses
2 pair dress shoes
6 informal pants or skirts
6 informal tops
3 pair casual shoes

Successful Images®

The corporate wardrobe is for the woman that has a job or works in an office which dictates a professional look. For example, if you work in a legal office, the corporate wardrobe is for you. If you are a salesperson or have a job that puts you in the eyes of the clients, the corporate wardrobe is appropriate.

The non-corporate wardrobe is for the woman who has a more casual job or works in a more casual atmosphere. For example, if you work in a department store, the non-corporate wardrobe will probably meet your clothing needs.

The appropriate wardrobe for you can usually be determined simply by noticing what other employees wear on the job, especially the employees you consider successful. Caution, however, that some employees may be "under-dressed" while others are "over-dressed." You must assess the properly dressed people.

PACKING FOR BUSINESS TRAVEL
FOR WOMEN

If you are like most people, the worst part of traveling is fitting everything you need into one suitcase. Following is information that will help you on your next trip: How to pack a week's worth of clothing into a **briefcase**. Why carry a large suitcase when you don't have to?!

1. Plan For Your Trip

   You must first analyze the purpose of your trip in order to plan the proper wardrobe. For example, if you will be doing a lot of walking, plan your wardrobe around comfortable shoes. Your shoes should be the foundation of your travel needs.

2. Wear the Right Clothing En Route

   You should wear a suit in a neutral or basic color, one that will coordinate well with the rest of the items you pack. You will get the most out of a solid color suit. Also wear a print blouse to add life to your look, and wear the most valuable jewelry you plan to take (don't pack it!). You may wish to carry a raincoat.

3. Build Your Wardrobe

   The following items, combined with the suit you wear during travel, will offer you a different business outfit for every day of the week, and also clothing for "off work" hours:

   a. Shoes (same color as you will wear in travel or a coordinating color)
   b. Skirt (to coordinate with the jacket you will wear; solid or subtle print)
   c. Two-piece print dress (you will be able to wear the pieces together or separately if the color coordinates with your other clothing
   d. Two solid blouses (one dressy, one casual; different colors will give your wardrobe greater variety)
   e. Camisole (one that can be worn out in the evening)
   f. Slacks or knit top (to coordinate with slacks and skirt)
   g. Sweater or knit top (to coordinate with slacks and skirt)
   h. Stockings
   i. Underwear
   j. Night wear
   k. Jewelry
   l. Scarves (at least two; one to be worn at the neck, and a longer scarf that can be worn as a belt or around the neck)
   m. Belt

4. Pack Your 3-Inch Briefcase

   a. Put your blouses and the top of your dress together by slipping the sleeves into each other. Do not button the blouses. When you are done you will have "one" layered blouse. Fold it in half lengthwise, then roll from the bottom.

   b. Hold the skirts together, with the most crush-resistant skirt on the inside, and fold into thirds lengthwise. Roll from the waistband to the hem.

   c. Roll the sweater as you did the blouse.

   d. Place all of the small items (stockings, underwear, jewelry, belt) inside your shoes.

e. Pack all of the necessary toiletries (in travel size containers) and makeup inside a small clutch that you can use as an evening bag. Place it and a travel size hair dryer in a larger handbag that you can carry separately.

f. Arrange all of the above items (except the clutch) in your briefcase, with the shoes on top, soles up, so your clothes do not get soiled. (You may even want to put the shoes in a plastic bag.)

Bon voyage!

Extra tips

• Select tailored clothing that will mix and match easily for your trip.

• Depending on the amount of business you will be conducting on your trip, you may wish to pack more blouses or dresses, and leave the slacks and sweater at home.

• To eliminate wrinkles in clothing while traveling:

a. Hang garments in the bathroom while showering. The steam from the shower will steam out wrinkles.

b. Sligthly dampen wrinkled areas, and blow dry with your hair dryer. The combination of water and heat will act as a steam iron, and wrinkles will disappear.

CHAPTER VI

BODY LANGUAGE AND BUSINESS ETIQUETTE

The purpose of this chapter is to teach you how to put your best foot forward at all times. By doing this, all the people with whom you come in contact will know that you are **someone**, that you believe in yourself, that you like the person you see in the mirror. Both body language and business etiquette will help convey your confidence and professionalism to others. Eighty percent of success has been proven to lie in attitude. Let your body language and business etiquette reflect your positive attitude.

Body Language

You probably make many body gestures without even knowing that you're making them. Think about the habits that you have. Perhaps you stand with your hands behind your back while talking to others. This conveys confidence and control to those around you. Playing with your cuffs or cuff links, or walking with your hands in your pockets, thumbs exposed, tell others that you have a big ego and you need special attention.

Sometime while you are sitting in a room, take time to examine others. In a typical business situation, there are usually a few minutes of small talk before a meeting actually starts. The subject may be last night's ballgame or the weather. During this time, everyone is evaluating each other to see how confident they are. They are looking for signs of weakness and nervousness, trying to figure out if someone is upset or happy. **This is the most crucial time to show your confidence and positive attitude.**

When you are talking to someone, does the person ever make hand-to-face gestures? For example, does he stroke his chin? If he does, pat yourself on the back, because he is listening intently to every word you are saying. If you are a sales person and your client starts stroking his chin, you are almost guaranteed to make the sale.

You should not cross your arms in front of you. This gesture expresses negativity; it indicates that you have a closed mind and are unwilling to listen to anything that conflicts with your own opinions. Also, research shows that a listener, just by folding his arms, reduces retention of information by 38 percent as compared to a listener who leaves his arms "open." You also shouldn't clench your hands into fists. This gives others the impression that you are frustrated and under stress.

When you walk, walk with confidence. A confident walk consists of kicking the leg out from the hip, not from the knee. This walk looks more sophisticated. It will also get you where you are going in a shorter period of time because your stride is longer. A friendly smile, upright posture, and a sense of energy will tell others that you are forthright, confident, and contained. Carry your briefcase in your left hand so you are ready to shake hands and get down to business or pleasure, whichever is the case. Women should not carry both a purse and a briefcase, as it weighs them down and gives them an unprofessional look. Don't hunch your shoulders or take small steps when walking. This shows others that you are timid and vulnerable. Hold your shoulders back and look straight ahead with a smile on your face. This is a very friendly and confident look.

Eye contact is extremely important. It is the key to being believed, trusted and respected. Someone once said, "Eyes are the window to one's soul." Have you ever talked to someone that was wearing sunglasses indoors? Wasn't it difficult to trust that person and believe what he was saying? You felt like he was hiding something from you. You will give others that same feeling if you wear sunglasses indoors. This applies not only to sunglasses, but any tinted glasses and also false-looking colored contact lenses. Your natural eye color is the most beautiful. Don't hide your eyes! Accent them by wearing the right clothing colors.

Eye movement also conveys different emotions and feelings. If your pupils are dilated, it means you are excited about something. Perhaps someone has just signed a valuable contract for your product. Your eyes will reflect your excitment. Constricted pupils indicate just the opposite – disappointment or regret. Did you just lose a contract? Your eyes will show it. Even eye blinking reveals emotions you think you are hiding. If you blink your eyes fourteen or more times per minute, you are probably nervous and feeling a lot of stress. If you blink ten times or less per minute, chances are you are tired or bored.

Eye contact with the person to whom you are talking is very important. Don't let your eyes wander around the room to focus on other people or other objects. Give the person your undivided attention. This shows respect and interest, and it also shows that you have confidence in yourself, that you believe in what you are saying.

Facial expressions can do a lot for you. A smile, widened eyes, and raised eyebrows all cause interest, excitement, and agreeability. You will come across as more trustworthy, interesting, and approachable by using many different facial expressions. People will concentrate more on your face than on any other part of you. Let your face help you make the first impression that you want to make. Politicans and actors use facial expressions every day to get the results they want.

Do you have any nervous habits when you are around others? Perhaps you bounce or constantly tap your foot. Some people click a pen, tap a pencil, or make any other repetitive noise. If you do any of these things, you have a nervous habit. Force yourself to overcome this. It is distracting, it shows a lack of confidence, and the person whom you are with will also be uncomfortable.

Many times you will see a man sitting at his desk with his hands behind his head. This makes him appear condescending and arrogant, even if he isn't. Women can't get away with this, either. She ends up looking rude, and she may even look like she's trying to imitate a man.

Have you ever seen anyone sitting at a desk with their hands in a "steeple" position? This expresses a healthy sense of power and position. This kind of positive power can give you energy and a feeling of direction. If, for some reason, you are ever being verbally attacked, a high steeple may help you defend yourself. The power impression will many times persuade the other person to cool off.

A true smile goes a long, long way. Don't be afraid to enjoy what you are doing and to let others know you enjoy it. Let your smile reflect your pride, feeling of accomplishment, and confidence.

As mentioned before, you probably do a lot of the things mentioned here and don't even realize that you're doing them. Take some time to practice in front of a mirror to see just what it is you do. What "right" gestures do you do? Keep on doing them! What "wrong" gestures have become a habit for you? Get rid of these! You may want to enlist the help of a friend who will give you honest feedback. Sometimes it is very hard for people to analyze themselves honestly. Don't be ashamed to ask for help!

Perhaps some "right" gestures were mentioned that are not part of your natural actions. Practice these gestures and they will soon become a part of you. They will feel strange at first, but the results you will see in the end will be worth it. Anything you do for 21 consecutive days will become a habit for life – it is a proven fact. By making gestures work for you, you can't help but succeed in your career and in your personal life!

Business Etiquette

Now that you know how to use body language to make a great first impression, you are ready to top off your skills with a little business etiquette.

Punctuality is a great beginning for any meeting, professional or social. Being on time shows courtesy and respect for the other person's time.

Shaking hands clearly establishes the boundaries of any relationship. Both men and women should always shake hands with other people. The custom of a man waiting until a woman offers her hand is a dated one.

Make your handshake "say" what you want it to say. A good handshake is one where palms touch, and three or four good shakes come from the elbow. It should express friendliness, confidence, and competence. Direct eye contact also does a lot for a good handshake. Weak handshakes are always received negatively.

If a man gives a businesswoman a soft handshake or only takes her fingers, he is telling her that he is treating her differently than he would a businessman. He may also be saying that he is a womanizer or a manipulator. Also, a clentched hand gives the impression of frustration and stress. A handshake that is too powerful gives the wrong impression, too. Be careful not to hurt the person whose hand you are shaking. If you are friendly with the person whom you are greeting, a two-handed handshake (one hand on the person's arm) will express the feeling of friendship.

Make sure that your manners fit the situation. A lot of people worry about this subject, but there is really nothing difficult about having good manners. Manners are 75 percent common sense and 25 percent thinking of others.

Be a good host or hostess. Someday you may find yourself in a position where a person who is involved in the situation is very uncomfortable. Perhaps he is not used to being in the particular type of situation he is in, and therefore does not know how to act. Or maybe he is from a foreign country and just does not know the American customs that are used in business or social functions. If you go out of your way to make him feel at ease, you will both feel better, and things will go a lot more smoothly.

You may not realize it, but you probably establish your own "territory" for every situation you are in. All people like to have their own personal space. As a rule of thumb, your area extends out about five feet in front of you. Within this area lies the "intimate zone," which begins at about 20 inches from you. Be especially careful of someone else's intimate zone. Getting too close to people can often cause discomfort and make both of you feel awkward. For example, think of how you sometimes feel uncomfortable when stepping into an elevator. Elevators are so small that if anyone else is in there, you are probably invading each other's territories.

If you move into a person's intimate zone too soon, you will most likely put that person on the defensive. No matter how passive a person you are, you are still in the other person's territory. It is best to stay within a 1-1/2 to 5 foot "personal zone" in which both of you will feel more comfortable and less threatened.

It is also possible to invade another person's territory with your belongings. For example, by laying your coat on a chair, you are claiming that chair as your space. Be especially careful when you are in another person's office. Do not use their desk as your temporary desk while you are meeting. If you need the use of some desk space, ask permission before using it.

No one should ever put their feet on a desk. This position is too laid back. It is also rude if someone else is in the office with them.

When you need to meet with someone, take into consideration the location of the meeting. It will be to your advantage to hold the meeting in your office. This is the place in which you feel most comfortable because you are in familiar surroundings. Likewise, the other person's office will work to his advantage. If you cannot meet in your own office, perhaps you can pick a neutral location, such as a conference room.

Also make note of where you sit during the meeting. If you want to make direct eye contact with the other person, be sure to sit across from him. If you do not wish to have this direct eye contact, then consider a shoulder to shoulder seating arrangement.

If you find yourself constantly glancing at your watch, you are being very rude to the other person. This action strongly communicates that you are bored, you have better things to do, and you have no interest in what the person is saying. If you can't break this habit, perhaps you should take off your watch and put it in your pocket until the meeting is over, unless of course, you have another appointment to keep.

To help relax the person to whom you're speaking, nod your head occasionally. The other person will soon start nodding with you. Not only is he now more comfortable with the situation, but he is also listening better because you have relieved some of the tension. However, don't overdo it, as it will become obvious. Nod just enough that you generate understanding.

Eighty percent of the information that a person retains is related to your appearance. If you can improve your appearance, attitude, and behavior, you will be more successful. Just as a company's products and services present a specific image of the company, your appearance, posture, and gestures also present a specific image. **You** are an important element in the achievement of your goals. The same thing applies if you are interviewing for a position. It has been proven that a person's appearance accounts for 60 percent in an interview.

Stress alone can contribute to your lack of success. If you have a problem with stress, try some of these hints: If you are alone, stand up and stretch your arms straight out at shoulder length, with your fingers spread as far apart as possible. Hold this position for one to two minutes. If you are with others, press your fingertips together, keeping all of your fingers spread apart. Now bounce your palms together while holding your fingers in this position. Others in the room will think you are in deep thought about what is being said. Not only will it help relax you, but it will also alleviate sweaty palms.

All of this information can help you be more successful in both your personal and professional lives. Do not be afraid to stand in front of the mirror, and work on your weak points. **You have a choice!** You can keep your life as it is, or you can improve it by changing those parts of it with which you are not satisfied.

THE BUSINESS LOOK – DOS AND DON'TS
FOR MEN

Following are some general dos and don'ts that you should keep in mind for your best business look. Remember these points when you are getting dressed for work or shopping for new clothing and accessories.

1. **DON'T** have a mustache or a beard (unless you are trying to camouflage a nose or lip problem). Wearing facial hair is like wearing a mask. You are telling people that you are hiding something. To be successful, you must have an open, trustworthy and approachable look.

2. **DO** wear the white of your season for a business/dress shirt to achieve the most conservative look. This is always the safest look in business.

3. **DO** wear natural fabrics: 100% silk ties, 100% wool or wool blend suits, cotton shirts, etc.

4. **DO** wear only two-piece suits, which is the business look of the 80's, unless you are in a profession such as banking or law.

5. **DO** pay attention to the types and styles of clothing worn by the serious executive men and women of your organization. This look has probably helped to get them where they are today.

6. **DO** choose dark colors, either solid or pinstripe, when dressing for maximum professionalism.

7. **DO** wear businesslike clothes to the office. Your clothing should not be too casual. It will send the message that you would rather be outdoors playing than at work. Stay away from open-collar shirts, turtlenecks, and short-sleeve shirts.

8. **DO** wear clothes that fit properly. If your collar is too tight or too loose, it will look like you are wearing someone else's clothing.

9. **DON'T** spend a lot of money on fad clothing, because most fad clothing is not appropriate for the office. Not only is the style usually not businesslike, but fad clothing quickly goes out of style. It is a poor investment.

10. **DO** tie your neckties properly. When a tie is properly tied, the longer end of it will lie just at the top of your belt or at the middle of your belt, never higher or lower.

11. **DO** wear ties that are 3¼" to 3½" at the widest part. This width will never go out of style. Ties that are narrower or wider will.

12. **DO** make sure that the lapels on your suits and sport coats match the width of the tie – 3¼" to 3½". That way the suit will never look dated, even if you have owned it for 8 to 10 years.

13. **DO** have your shirts professionally laundered. The difference in the way the shirt will look on you is incredible.

14. **DON'T** wear too much jewelry. A man should wear one ring to work – his wedding band. Class rings should not be worn to the office as they tend to give people the impression that you wish you were still in school. Flashy diamond rings and pinkie rings will give the image of a con man or gambler. They are fine for evening wear, and should be worn then. Don't wear bracelets or neck chains to work. Also, watchbands should be kept as simple as possible. The more slender the better. The watch should also have a sophisticated look to it. "Sport" watches – large, plastic watches with timers and alarms – should be saved for casual wear.

15. **DON'T** wear clothes that sport the designer's name in view of others. Don't promote someone else – promote yourself!

16. **DO** wear good quality shirts or shirts made of heavier material so that any chest hair will not show through. Otherwise, always wear a T-shirt.

17. **DON'T** wear short sleeve shirts unless you have a "physical" job, such as that of a repairman or

construction engineer. Short sleeves are appropriate in jobs where you would roll up your sleeves.

18. **DON'T** fear wearing the same nice pieces of clothing more than once a week. People rarely notice that you have worn the same thing again. What they do notice is that you either are or are not nicely dressed.

19. **DO** camouflage figure flaws. Learn how to hide your figure problems; don't accent them.

20. **DON'T** wear denim to the office. Denim does not work in business.

21. **DON'T** forget your feet. A great wardrobe is easily ruined by shoes that are the wrong color, are an inappropriate style, or are poorly maintained.

22. **DON'T** be self-conscious or ashamed of wearing eyeglasses, and don't underestimate the effect they have on your overall appearance. A frame with a businesslike look to it can make you look more mature and authoritative.

23. **DO** be aware that you will be viewed more from the waist up than from the waist down. Therefore, if you can afford only some high quality pieces, make sure the pieces are coats, blazers, sweaters, etc. If your pants fit correctly, the fact that they are less expensive will probably go unnoticed.

24. With regard to foulard ties, the smaller the foulard, the more sophisticated the tie.

25. **DON'T** ever have the attitude that your clothing need not be perfect, even for one day. You should say to yourself every morning, "Today is the day that the boss wants to see me about my future with the company."

26. **DO** project your best image at all times in order to be as successful as possible. Even if you are just going to a movie, wear casual slacks instead of jeans. Price doesn't vary much from casual slacks to jeans, but there is no comparison of the impact on your image. Casual slacks say more positive things than jeans do. (Nicely styled designer jeans can be worn, but be sure that they are well pressed.)

27. **DON'T** cut yourself in half with color, such as wearing a light shirt and dark slacks, if you want to appear taller. One solid color from head to toe elongates the body.

28. **DO** wear a name tag on your right side when you need to wear one. This makes it easier for the person shaking your hand to read your name tag.

29. **DO** carry a briefcase in your left hand. Keep your right hand available for a quick, strong handshake.

30. **DO** check your appearance in a 3-way mirror before buying any new piece of clothing or accessory. You are viewed straight on only 20% of the time. The other 80% of the time you are viewed from different angles.

31. If you are constantly wearing out the seat or knees of your pants before the rest of the suit wears out, have lining put in your pants to prolong their life. It is relatively inexpensive.

32. **DO** carry a good quality pen, but don't overdo it. For example, a solid gold pen is too flashy and can actually distract others from concentrating on what you are saying or selling.

33. **DO** carry a clean and ironed handkerchief daily. Paper tissues just don't make the grade.

34. **DO** carry a good quality leather wallet and pocket calendar. The more slender these items, the more sophisticated and professional.

35. **DO** keep your business calling card in close reach and easy access.

36. Cologne is not appropriate for the office. However, if you wish to wear it, wear a very little amount so that you are not overwhelming. (The smell should not remain after you have ridden in an elevator, for instance.)

37. **DO** be aware that people notice your smile every time they look at you. If your teeth are not what they should be, whether it is a health or cosmetic problem, see your dentist.

38. **DO** look good 24 hours a day!

THE BUSINESS LOOK – DOS AND DON'TS
FOR WOMEN

Following are some general dos and don'ts that you should keep in mind for your best business look. Remember these points when you are getting dressed for work or shopping for new clothing and accessories.

1. **DO** pay attention to the types and styles of clothing worn by the serious executive men and women of your organization. This look has probably helped to get them where they are today.

2. **DON'T** carry a briefcase **and** a purse. You will look like you are loaded down. Slip a small purse inside your briefcase. Use the purse to hold your money, makeup, and comb.

3. **NEVER** wear slacks to work. Always wear a suit, skirt, or appropriate dress.

4. **DON'T** allow your slip to show through pleats in your skirt or dress. Wear a slip to match that pleat.

5. **DO** wear sheer blouses with a slip or camisole underneath. Make sure that the undergarment is not a color that will show through your blouse.

6. **DON'T** wear dangle earrings to the office. They are too sexy for work. Also, it is very annoying to anyone you speak with on the phone, as these earrings swing and bang against the receiver. Keep them for evening or casual wear.

7. **DON'T** wear evening wear to the office. It does not belong in the office. For women, strappy shoes are too sexy for the office. Keep business shoes simple – a pump is best.

8. **DO always** wear hosiery. It is never too hot and you are never too tan to go without hose.

9. **DO** match the color of hose or socks to slacks or skirt and shoes. Do not contrast! The look is too extreme.

10. **DO** wear the white of your season for a business/dress blouse to achieve the most conservative look. This is always the safest look in business.

11. **DON'T** wear starched cotton blouses. The look is too masculine.

12. **DO** add a belt when you wear a skirt or slacks. It is simple to do and it pulls your whole outfit together.

13. **DON'T** assume that your suits have to look like men's clothing in order for you to appear professional and authoritative. You are still a woman! Blouses come in many different styles that are appropriate for business women: V-neck, wraps, etc.

14. **DON'T** wear denim to the office. Denim does not work in business.

15. **DON'T** spend a lot of money on fad clothing, because most fad clothing is not appropriate for the office. Not only is the style usually not businesslike, but fad clothing quickly goes out of style. It is a poor investment.

16. **DO** wear businesslike clothes to the office. Your clothing should not be too casual. It will send the message that you would rather be outdoors playing than at work. Don't wear sundresses to work unless a coordinating jacket is kept on all day.

17. **DO** wear clothes that fit properly. Blouses should not be so low-cut that they are either too sexy or undergarments are showing. You can not be taken seriously as a business person when you are not dressed properly for your position.

18. **DON'T** wear too much jewelry. If you do, each piece will lose its interest. Simple is elegant. Your wedding and engagement rings on one finger, and one ring on the other hand is appropriate. Class rings should not be worn to the office as they tend to give people the impression that you wish you were still in school.

19. **DO** project your best image at all times in order to be as successful as possible. Even if you are just going to a movie, wear casual slacks instead of jeans. Price does not vary much from casual slacks to jeans, but there is no comparison of the impact on your image. Casual slacks say more positive things than jeans do. (Nicely styled designer jeans can be worn, but be sure that they are well pressed.)

20. **DON'T** wear clothes that sport the designer's name in view of others. Don't promote someone else – promote yourself!

21. **DON'T** fear wearing the same nice pieces of clothing more than once a week. People rarely notice that you have worn the same thing again. What they do notice is that you either are or are not nicely dressed.

22. **DO** camouflage figure flaws. Learn how to hide your figure problems; don't accent them.

23. **DON'T** cut yourself in half with color, such as wearing a light blouse and dark skirt if you want to appear taller. One solid color from head to toe elongates the body.

24. **DON'T** forget your feet. A great wardrobe is easily ruined by shoes that are the wrong color, are an inappropriate style, or are poorly maintained.

25. **DON'T** be self-conscious or ashamed of wearing eyeglasses, and don't underestimate the effect they have on your overall appearance. A frame with a businesslike look to it can make your look more mature and authoritative.

26. **DO** wear a name tag on your right side when you need to wear one. This makes it easier for the person shaking your hand to read your name tag.

27. **DO** carry a briefcase in your left hand. Keep your right hand available for a quick, strong handshake.

28. **DO** check your appearance in a 3-way mirror before buying any new piece of clothing or accessory. You are viewed straight on only 20% of the time. The other 80% of the time you are viewed from different angles.

29. **DO** be aware that you will be viewed more from the waist up than from the waist down. Therefore, if you can afford only some high quality pieces, make sure the pieces are coats, blazers, sweaters, etc. If your pants or skirt fit correctly, the fact that they are less expensive will probably go unnoticed.

30. **DON'T** ever have the attitude that your clothing need not be perfect, even for one day. You should say to yourself every morning, "Today is the day that the boss wants to see me about my future with the company."

31. **DO** carry a good quality pen, but don't overdo it. For example, a solid gold pen is too flashy and can actually distract others from concentrating on what you are saying or selling.

32. **DO** carry a good quality leather wallet and pocket calendar. The more slender these items, the more sophisticated and professional.

33. **DO** keep your business calling card in close reach and easy access.

34. Cologne is not appropriate for the office. However, if you wish to wear it, wear a very little amount so that you are not overwhelming. (The smell should not remain after you have ridden in an elevator, for instance.)

35. **DO** be aware that people notice your smile every time they look at you. If your teeth are not what they should be, whether it is a health or cosmetic problem, see your dentist.

36. **DO** look good 24 hours a day!

CHAPTER VII
THE TOTAL LOOK

ASSESSING YOUR PRESENT VISUAL IMAGE

Everything that you wear sends out a visual image, or message, to the people whom you deal with every day. Therefore, it is very important that you send out the most positive message possible. The first step toward making your message its strongest is to assess your present visual image.

To do this, stand in front of a full-length mirror and assess yourself **honestly**. What does your clothing say about your:

- Economic level _____
- Education level _____
- Trustworthiness _____
- Social position _____
- Level of sophistication _____
- Economic heritage _____
- Social heritage _____
- Educational heritage _____
- Success _____
- Moral character _____

Don't be ashamed if your visual image is not what you want it to be. You are not alone. Most of us have room for some improvements. You will learn, step by step, how to be your very best with only a little bit of effort on your part. Most people do not realize how easy it is to look great all the time. Now you, too, will know the secret to successful living.

You have heard the saying, "You are what you eat." Well, it is also true that "You are what you wear." If you are meeting someone for the first time, the only immediate image of you that person has is the image that he sees. In the first thirty seconds, he evaluates you on every one of the points listed above. It is hard to believe, but studies have shown that what you wear counts 60% in an interview. Education and past job experience make up the other 40%. In business, time is money. Use even these first thirty seconds to your advantage. Let your appearance score professional points for you. People who are well-dressed and well-groomed earn more, are promoted faster, and are perceived as more competent than those who are not.

Not long ago a research study was done to either prove or disprove that clothing makes a difference in the way people treat each other. In this particular study, a man was asked to stand on a very busy street corner three mornings in a row. Each day he was asked to stop pedestrians and say to them: "I forgot my wallet at home this morning and I don't even have enough money to take the bus to work. Can you help me out?"

On the first morning he wore a three piece suit, and he received comments like, "That's happened to me before; here's a five. Take a taxi to work. Next time we meet you can buy me a drink." The man made $360 that morning. (Please do not consider this as a new career for yourself.)

On the second morning the man wore a sport jacket with a tie, and he used the same line on people passing by. This time he received up to only $1.00 per person and comments like, "Here's money for the bus. Have a nice day." He made $150 that day. Still not bad!

On the third morning the same man appeared on the same street corner and used the same line, but this time he was wearing a pullover shirt and jeans. The most he was given by any one person was 25 cents, and he heard many comments such as, "Go find yourself a job." He made $40 that day.

It is very obvious that people show more respect to others who look professional. They show more respect to people who look like themselves (the people who gave the $5 bills), or who look like successful people.

Another example to stress the importance of image is to examine what happens to children based on how they look. The results of a study conducted over many years show that children who are dressed nicely are treated better and given more attention and care than children who are not. These children grow up to be more self-confident, they do better in college, and they land higher paying positions once they enter the job market.

Do not get the impression that education or job experience is not important. It certainly is. But it takes years to establish educational credentials and accumulate a good business sense. An image is something that is created and evaluated immediately. Your image is a way of wearing your credentials on the outside, a way of establishing credibility, integrity, competence, intelligence, and success.

Remember, everything that you wear makes a statement about you. It is impossible to go to your closet and choose clothing that doesn't say **something**. Since you are making a statement, or sending a message about yourself all the time, why not always send the best message possible, for any situation!

ACHIEVEMENT DRESSING

Achievement dressing focuses on choosing the wardrobe that is best for you. Six easy rules will help you become a successful achievement dresser:

1. **Start with a wardrobe strategy** – From the information contained in Chapter 5, you now know what types of clothing you need for your lifestyle. You should also be aware of what items are missing from your present wardrobe.

2. **Concentrate on "build-on" pieces** – By having many build-on pieces, such as pants, jackets, and shirts, mixing and matching these items will give you a seemingly larger wardrobe. You will have the most for the least amount of money.

3. **Create color strategy** – By building your wardrobe around the colors that are best for you, your whole wardrobe will coordinate. Not only will you have the largest variety of items to mix and match, but dressing will be easier because everything will blend well. You learned the proper colors for your hair, skin, and eye color in Chapter 2. Make those colors work for you.

4. **Purchase styles to fit your body shape and personality** – Chapters 3 and 4 helped you understand your body shape and personality type. Now that you know which styles are best for you, you can accent the good points of your figure and easily disguise any figure flaws. Doing this will help you to achieve your very best look.

5. **Buy quality** – When purchasing clothing, buy the best quality that you can afford. Good quality clothing will make you look better, and it will last longer.

6. **Use simple but interesting accessories** – A man's accessories are his ties, shirts, and pocket squares. A woman's accessories are her blouses, scarves, and jewelry. By owning and wearing a variety of these items, which are less expensive than suits, you can inexpensively change your whole look. Choosing simple accessories will help them maintain their interest.

A MAN'S OVERALL IMAGE
LOOK YOUR BEST FROM HEAD TO TOE

HAIR

To look your best, your hair style should be based on the shape of your face. Of course, the type of hair you have (thick or thin, coarse or fine) plays a part in the right style for you. (Face shape and appropriate hair styles are talked about in Part II of this book.)

Your hair should be kept neatly trimmed at all times.

Be sure to comb your hair as often as necessary (but don't get carried away). If you use any sprays or lotions in your hair, use as little as possible.

Facial hair is not a business look; but if you feel the need to keep facial hair, make sure that the style suits the shape of your face, and always keep it well groomed.

If your hair needs more attention, make note here of what you should be doing differently.

NOTE: _____

_____

SHIRT

Colors that look good on you should be chosen for your shirts, because they are worn close to the face. In the Color Analysis section of this workbook, you learned that your "season" of colors has light shades. These should be used for your shirts.

Patterns add interest to a shirt, but the look of them is always less formal than that of a solid. Subtle patterns are suitable for business, but noticeable patterns should be limited to casual and social clothing. Patterns in shirts should be appropriate for the suits and jackets that you wear them with. Be very careful when combining patterns.

The shirt fabric should correspond well with the finish of your suits and jackets.

Be sure that the shirt collar fits you properly. A collar that is too tight or too loose will give the impression that the shirt belongs to someone else. To find the proper length of your shirt sleeve, measure the length of your arm from the center of the nape of your neck along your shoulder down to your wristbone, where the edge of the cuff should lie.

Collars come in many styles these days. Choose a style that accents the shape of your face. For example, if you have a narrow jaw, a rounded collar is probably better for you. The collar style that is best for you is dependent upon what shape your face is. See Part II of the workbook.

Be sure that your cuffs also fit properly. They should extend about a half inch beyond your jacket sleeve, no more. Cuffs that are well-pressed will give you a very polished look.

Make note of your collar size and sleeve length here.

NOTE: _____

_____

TIES

The color of your tie should always coordinate with the color of your shirt and jacket. A very friendly, yet authoritative color for a tie is red. Be sure to choose a red that falls within your season.

Patterned ties add "life" to a suit. Foulard is nice, as is a stripe. When choosing a stripe, the most sophisticated stripe is one in which all of the stripes are exactly the same width. Other, more bold patterns are on the market today, but be careful to wear them with suits and shirts that are plain.

A tie that is 100% silk will look the best and last the longest. It is also much easier to tie, and it lies better.

The size of the tie's knot can vary, depending on how you tie it. Be sure that the knot size suits the shirt collar, your face shape, and your body proportions.

The end of the tie should come either to the top of the belt or to the middle of the belt, never higher or lower.

If the widest part of your tie is 3¼″ to 3½″, the tie will never go out of style. Ties that are wider or narrower will. If you are broad-chested, a broader tie will make you look more slim. If you are thin, choose a narrower tie.

Comments about your ties:

NOTE: _____

_____

SUIT COAT OR JACKET

Suits of the darker colors in your palette will give you your most authoritative look; however, suits of lighter colors are fine, too, when worn for appropriate occasions.

Patterns in suits should be conservative in all but appropriate occasions. Be sure that the pattern is matched at the seams. Otherwise, the suit will have a very cheap look to it.

A wool or wool blend is best for a suit and it will last the longest. A light-weight wool, wool blend, or cotton blend is good for warmer months.

Your suit cut should match your physical build. Avoid fad cuts, as they will become outdated quickly.

Make sure that your suit fits properly. A good tailor is as important as a good quality suit.

To find your perfect jacket length, have someone measure you from the base of your neck to the floor with no shoes on. Divide this measurement exactly in half. The halfway point is where your jacket should end.

The edge of your sleeve should just cover your wristbone. Your shirt cuff should show by no more than one-half inch.

Your jacket should not be trimmed with contrasting thread. The look is too extreme. Also, be sure that the buttons are not cheap looking. No matter how expensive the suit is, cheap buttons will lower the overall look of quality.

The width of the lapel should match the width of the tie at its widest point. The lapels, too, should measure between 3¼″ and 3½″ to never go out of style. If you have an older jacket with wider lapels, have a tailor narrow them. The jacket will no longer look outdated.

Make any notes of your perfect jacket length here. Also note any other information about suits as they apply to you. (For example: Are the lapels too wide? Are the buttons of good quality?)

NOTE: _____

_____

PANTS

When purchasing slacks that aren't part of a suit, choose from the basic and neutral colors or your season's palette.

Stick to a solid or a conservative pattern, such as pin stripes or a barely noticeable plaid. Stripes will give your legs a longer appearance, while plaid will make them look shorter.

The fabric of your pants should coordinate with the fabric of the jackets with which they're being worn.

Pant leg widths vary as time goes on. Be sure that you are wearing a width that is in style today. Better yet, choose a conservative width that won't go out of style.

Make sure that your pants fit properly. Don't give anyone the impression that you're wearing someone else's clothes.

The pant leg should just touch the top of your shoes in the front, and you may have it taper down one-half inch longer in the back. The taper will help keep your pant legs from falling into your shoes.

Be careful with cuffs. If you are tall and want to appear shorter, then cuffs are for you. If you are short, you should stay away from cuffs, as they will make you look even shorter.

Write any pants comments here. (For example: I should never wear cuffs. My pant legs should be taken in.)

NOTE: _____

_____

SHOES   Dress loafers and oxfords are both good for business. Wear colors that coordinate with the color of your suits and pants.

Shoes made of good quality leather will last for years.

Be sure to keep your shoes well-polished. Your whole look can be ruined with shoes that have not been maintained.

Have worn-down heels replaced.

Do your shoes need any attention?

NOTE: _____

_____

ACCESSORIES

Belt – A good quality leather belt that corresponds with your clothing and shoe color will pull your whole look together. Be sure the belt buckle is made of your season's metal (yellow gold or white gold).

Socks – Socks should blend with the color of your pants. Over-the-calf socks should be worn so that your legs do not show when you are sitting.

Glasses – Choose a frame that accents your face shape.

Jewelry – Men should wear only a wedding ring to work. A handsome watch with the slimmest band possible is the best look. Cuff links can be a nice touch as long as they're not too flashy. Be careful not to look too ostentatious for your particular type of client and/or region (e.g., cuff links work in the northeast but not in the midwest).

Comments about accessories:

NOTE: _____

_____

PERSONAL GROOMING   Have your shirts, ties, and suits professionally cleaned and pressed. Be sure that your clothes aren't torn, missing buttons, fraying, etc.

If you have a dandruff problem, take extra precautions when washing your hair. If necessary, see a dermatologist.

Keep your clothes lint free. In lieu of a lint brush, you can use adhesive tape. Simply blot fabric with the sticky side of the tape.

Do be conscious of any body odor you may have. If necessary, keep deodorant handy at work. Also be sure that your breath is not offensive.

A WOMAN'S OVERALL IMAGE
LOOK YOUR BEST FROM HEAD TO TOE

HAIR

To look your best, your hair style should be based on the shape of your face. Of course, the type of hair you have (thick or thin, coarse or fine) plays a part in the right style for you. (Face shape and appropriate hair styles are talked about in Part II of this book.)

Your hair should be styled as simply as possible, so that it is not hard to keep it looking good at all times. If you prefer long hair, it is more businesslike to have it pulled up.

Should you wish to color your hair, be sure to select a color that looks good with your skin color. The Color Analysis section of this book has suggestions for the color you should use.

Comb your hair as often as necessary. Hair spray should be used as lightly as possible. You don't want a "plastered" look.

If you are troubled with facial hair, you should carefully bleach or trim it, or, in severe cases, have it professionally removed.

If your hair needs more attention, make note here of what you should be doing differently.

NOTE: _____

_____

MAKEUP

It may come as a surprise, but even businessmen prefer to see businesswomen with at least a little bit of blush and lipstick. Color Analysis talks about the makeup colors that are right for you.

One thing to remember: Makeup for business should have a light, natural look. Save dramatic makeup for evening.

Makeup application guides follow at the end of this section.

If your makeup needs more attention, make some comments about it here.

NOTE: _____

_____

DRESSES AND BLOUSES

Colors that look good on you should be chosen for your dresses and blouses because they are worn close to the face. In the Color Analysis section of this book, you will learn what your "season" of colors is. Choose your most flattering colors from your season.

Patterns add interest to clothing. Subtle patterns are more suitable for business. Noticeable patterns should be limited to casual and social clothing. If you are pairing a dress or blouse with a jacket, the patterns should coordinate. Be very careful when combining patterns.

Sheer fabrics and clingy fabrics are not businesslike. Neither are garments that are too tight. Remember your position!

Necklines vary greatly on dresses and blouses. Don't wear anything that is very low-cut or very ruffly to work.

Be sure that your cuffs also fit properly. They should extend about a half inch beyond your jacket sleeve, no more.

Make any comments about your dresses and blouses here.

NOTE: _____

_____

SCARVES

Just as men can change the whole look of a suit by changing ties, you can change your whole look by adding or changing scarves.

Choose scarves in the colors of your palette. They will match every other garment you own.

Scarves can be tied many different ways, so even the same scarf can give you many different looks.

By wrapping two scarves together and then tying them as one scarf, you can easily pull together the contrasting colors of a skirt and blouse.

Scarves made of 100% silk will last the longest and are the easiest to tie.

Make comments here about any scarves you own, and different outfits they can be worn with.

NOTE: _____

_____

JACKETS

Jacket colors should be mostly of the basic and neutral colors of your palette, as these colors can be worn with almost any other colors you own. Be sure to choose a color that flatters your blouse color.

Patterns in suits should be conservative in all but appropriate occasions. Be sure that the pattern is matched at the seams. Otherwise, the suit will have a very cheap look to it.

A wool or wool blend is best and it will last the longest. A light-weight wool, wool blend, or cotton blend is good for warmer months.

Women's jackets come in many different cuts. Be sure to choose a cut that complements your figure.

No matter how expensive a jacket is, it will lose most of its look if it does not fit properly. Have your jackets altered to fit your figure.

Women's jackets come in a variety of lengths. Be careful that the bottom edge of the jacket does not fall at your widest part (for example, right on the hip line). This will only make you look wider. A jacket that is longer or shorter is good.

The edge of your sleeve should just cover your wristbone.

Lapel widths vary over the years, and can easily become outdated. Be sure that your lapel widths are the style of today. If your lapels are too wide, a good seamstress can take them in for you.

Make any notes about your suits here.

NOTE: _____

_____

SKIRTS

Skirt colors should be mostly of the basic and neutral colors of your palette, as these colors can be worn with almost any other colors you own. Be sure to choose a color that flatters your blouse and jacket colors.

Patterns should be kept rather conservative for business. Choose patterns that are the right size for your body. (If you are a small person, choose a small pattern; a large one will be too overwhelming. If you are a large person, choose a larger pattern.)

The fabric of your skirts should coordinate with the fabric of the jackets with which they're being worn.

Make sure that your skirts fit properly. Don't give anyone the impression that you're wearing someone else's clothes.

Skirts that come below the knee are best for business. If your legs are thin, the most flattering skirt length for you is that in which the hem falls just above the widest part of your leg. If your legs are heavy, the best length for you is that in which the hem falls above or below the heaviest part of your leg.

Make note here of your best skirt length, pattern size that is right for you, and any other comments.

NOTE: _____

_____

SHOES

The best business and dress shoe is the simple, classic pump. These shoes are so versatile that they are an asset to everything you wear them with.

Whichever shoe you decide to wear to work, it should be conservative. A closed toe shoe is most businesslike. Strappy shoes and sandals are inappropriate for the office.

Shoes made of good quality leather will last for years.

Be sure to keep your shoes well-polished. Your whole look can be ruined with shoes that have not been maintained.

Have worn-down heels replaced.

Do your shoes need any attention?

NOTE: _____

_____

ACCESSORIES

Belt – A good quality leather belt that corresponds with your clothing and shoe color will pull your whole look together. A stylish buckle will make you look right up to date.

Nylons/Socks – Nylons or socks should blend with the color of your slacks.

Glasses – Choose a frame that accents your face shape.

Jewelry – Remember: Simple is elegant. Don't overdo. Choose rather simple jewelry so that each piece does not lose its interest.

Comments about accessories:

NOTE: _____

_____

ORDER BLANK

SHOPPING GUIDES – Complete color pallets for all four seasons, as well as advice on purchasing the correct jewelry, eyeglasses, sunglasses, hair color, cosmetics, leather goods, clothing colors, etc. $10.00 each.

QUANTITY	PRICE	TOTAL
____	@ $10.00	$_____

BOOKS – YOUR MIRROR IMAGE Book $20.00 each.

QUANTITY	PRICE	TOTAL
____	@ $20.00	$_____

Sub-total $_____
Georgia Residents Add 7% Sales Tax $_____
Add $3.00 shipping $ 3.00

Grand Total $_____

Ship to:
Name_____
Address_____
_____
City/State_____Zip_____
Work #_____Home #_____

Your order must be accompanied by full payment.
SORRY – NO C.O.D. ORDERS
Please send check or money order to:

**Successful Images
5680 Hershinger Close
Duluth, GA   30097-6430**

For information, call:
(770) 232-7101

Price listing no. 6 – 6/98

NOTES

NOTES